SCHOLASTIC

ALL NEW

100 MATHS LESSONS

HOMEWORK & ASSESSMENT

YEAR 4

Scottish Primary 5

Ann Montague-Smith
and Claire Tuthill

Credits

Authors
Ann Montague-Smith
Claire Tuthill

Editor
Jo Kemp

Assistant Editor
Margaret Eaton

Illustrations
Andy Keylock

Series Designer
Catherine Mason

Designers
Melissa Leeke
Micky Pledge
Helen Taylor

Designed using Adobe InDesign

Published by Scholastic Ltd
Villiers House
Clarendon Avenue
Leamington Spa
Warwickshire CV32 5PR

www.scholastic.co.uk

Printed by Bell and Bain Ltd, Glasgow

3456789 8901234 5

British Library Cataloguing-in-Publication Data
A catalogue record for this book is available from the British Library.

ISBN 0-439-96516-0
ISBN 978-0439-96516-3

Contents

ASSESSMENT

Assessment: Summer half-term 1

Assessment: Summer half-term 2

End-of-year assessment

About the series

All New100 Maths Homework and Assessment Activities offers a complete solution to your planning and resourcing for maths homework and assessment activities. There are seven books in the series, one for each year group from Reception to Year 6.

Each *All New 100 Maths Homework and Assessment Activities* book contains approximately 60 homework activities, with activity sheets to take home, and assessments for each half-term, end of term and end of year.

The homework and assessment activities support planning based on the National Numeracy Strategy's medium-term plans, but using the language of the learning objectives for that year as they appear in the NNS *Framework for Teaching Mathematics* (DfEE, 1999).

About the homework activities

Each homework activity is presented as a photocopiable page, with some supporting notes for parents and helpers provided underneath the activity. Teacher's notes appear in grid format for each term at the beginning of each term's activities. There are unit references in the grid, which link the homework activities to the relevant units in the NNS medium-term plan. Page references are also given that correspond to the relevant activities in the sister book, *All New 100 Maths Lessons Year 4* (Scholastic). The grid is the only place in the book where the objectives and further detail about the homework are provided. When exactly the homework is set and followed up is left to your professional judgement.

Across the *All New 100 Maths Homework and Assessment Activities* series, the homework activities cover the range of homework types suggested by the National Numeracy Strategy. For Year 4, there are Maths to share activities, Homework activities, Maths homework and Puzzles to do at home.

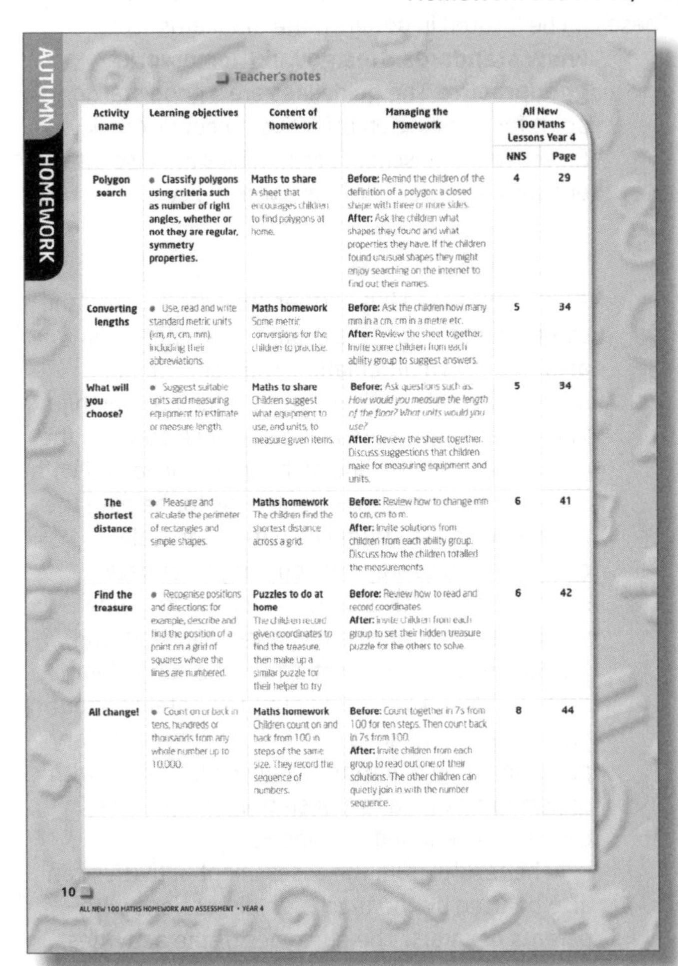

AUTUMN HOMEWORK

Teacher's notes

Activity name	Learning objectives	Content of homework	Managing the homework	All New 100 Maths Lessons Year 4	
				NNS	Page
Polygon search	• **Classify polygons using criteria such as number of right angles, whether or not they are regular, symmetry properties.**	**Maths to share** A sheet that encourages children to find polygons at home.	**Before:** Remind the children of the definition of a polygon: a closed shape with three or more sides. **After:** Ask the children what shapes they found and what properties they have. If the children found unusual shapes they might enjoy searching on the internet to find out their names.	4	29
Converting lengths	• Use, read and write standard metric units (km, m, cm, mm), including their abbreviations.	**Maths homework** Some metric conversions for the children to practise.	**Before:** Ask the children how many mm in a cm, cm in a metre etc. **After:** Review the sheet together. Invite some children from each ability group to suggest answers.	5	34
What will you choose?	• Suggest suitable units and measuring equipment to estimate or measure length.	**Maths to share** Children suggest what equipment to use, and units, to measure given items.	**Before:** Ask questions such as: *How would you measure the length of the floor? What units would you use?* **After:** Review the sheet together. Discuss suggestions that children make for measuring equipment and units.	5	34
The shortest distance	• Measure and calculate the perimeter of rectangles and simple shapes.	**Maths homework** The children find the shortest distance across a grid.	**Before:** Review how to change mm to cm, cm to m. **After:** Invite solutions from children from each ability group. Discuss how the children totalled the measurements.	6	41
Find the treasure	• Recognise positions and directions: for example, describe and find the position of a point on a grid of squares where the lines are numbered.	**Puzzles to do at home** The children record given coordinates to find the treasure, then make up a similar puzzle for their helper to try	**Before:** Review how to read and record coordinates. **After:** Invite children from each group to set their hidden treasure puzzle for the others to solve.	6	42
All change!	• Count on or back in tens, hundreds or thousands from any whole number up to 10,000.	**Maths homework** Children count on and back from 100 in steps of the same size. They record the sequence of numbers.	**Before:** Count together in 7s from 100 for ten steps. Then count back in 7s from 100. **After:** Invite children from each group to read out one of their solutions. The other children can quietly join in with the number sequence.	8	44

10

ALL NEW 100 MATHS HOMEWORK AND ASSESSMENT • YEAR 4

- **Maths to share activities** encourage the child to discuss the homework task with a parent or carer, and may, for example, involve the home context, or a game to be played with the carer.
- **Homework activities** are timed exercises which encourage the child to work rapidly.
- **Maths homework** activities allow the child to practise skills.
- **Puzzles to do at home** are investigations or problem-solving tasks. Again, the parent or carer is encouraged to be involved with the activity, offering support to the child, and discussing the activity and its outcomes with the child.

Using the homework activities

Each homework page includes a 'Helper note', which explains the aim of the homework and how the adult can support their child if he or she cannot get started. It is recommended that some form of homework diary be used alongside these activities, through which to establish an effective home-school dialogue about the children's enjoyment and understanding of the homework. A homework diary page is provided on page 8 of this book if you do not currently have another resource in use.

Teacher's notes

The teacher's notes appear at the start of each term's homework activities. They are presented in a grid format. The grid for the homework activities sets out the following:

- The title of the homework.
- Learning objectives: these are linked to the NNS medium-term plan. Where appropriate, the key objective(s) for that unit have a homework activity. This will help as part of on-going teacher assessment to show how well the children have understood the concepts being taught.
- The content of the homework: this shows the type of homework (Maths to share activities, Homework activities, Maths homework and Puzzles to do at home) and briefly describes the format and content of the activity.
- Managing the homework: this section provides 'before' and 'after' information for the teacher. The 'before' notes provide suggestions for ways to introduce and explain the homework before the children take it home. These notes might include a brief oral activity to undertake as preparation for the homework. The 'after' notes provide suggestions for how to manage the review of the homework when the children return with it to school. Suggestions include marking the work together, discussing strategies used for solving a problem, comparing solutions and playing a game as a class.
- NNS unit reference.
- Page link to *All New 100 Maths Lessons Year 4*. This will enable practitioners who are using this sister book to compare what is being taught that week with the homework, so that the teacher can decide which homework to choose and when to send it home.

Developing a homework policy

The homework activities have been written with the DfES 'Homework guidelines' in mind. These can be located in detail on the Standards Site: **www.standards.dfes.gov.uk/homework/goodpractice** The guidelines are a good starting point for planning an effective homework policy. Effective home-school partnerships are also vital in ensuring a successful homework policy.

AUTUMN HOMEWORK

Name Date

What will you choose?

- Look at each picture.
  - Imagine that you have to measure what is in the picture.
  - Write underneath which measuring equipment you would choose (ruler, metre stick or measuring tape).
  - Write which units you would choose.

I would measure this with a ______ I would use ______ units.

I would measure this with a ______ I would use ______ units.

I would measure this with a ______ I would use ______ units.

I would measure this with a ______ I would use ______ units.

I would measure this with a ______ I would use ______ units.

I would measure this with a ______ I would use ______ units.

Dear Helper
This activity helps your child to remember that the range of measuring equipment has different uses, and that the appropriate standard units need to be chosen for the size of what is measured. If your child is unsure about which units to use, discuss the size of a unit. Your child can then make a good estimate of which to choose. Challenge your child to think of more things that could be measured for length, what to measure them with, and the units to use. They could write this on the back of this sheet.

20 ALL NEW 100 MATHS HOMEWORK AND ASSESSMENT • YEAR 4 PHOTOCOPIABLE www.scholastic.co.uk

Encouraging home-school links

An effective working partnership with parents and carers makes a positive impact upon children's attainment in mathematics. The homework activities in this book are part of that partnership. Parents and carers are given guidance on what the homework is about, and on how to be involved with the activity. There are suggestions for helping the children who are struggling with a particular concept, such as ways of counting on or back mentally, and extension ideas for children who would benefit from slightly more advanced work. The homework that is set across the curriculum areas for Year 4 should amount to a total of about one and a half hours a week. The homework diary page, sent home with the homework activity with opportunities for a response from the parents/carers, can be found on page 8.

The results from the assessment activities can also be used by the teacher in discussions with parents or carers. The outcomes of the activities, which cover the key objectives taught that half-term, term or year, will give good evidence for the teacher and parents/carers about how well the child is performing for the year group.

Using the activities with *All New 100 Maths Lessons Year 4*

The activities, both homework and assessment, fit the planning within *All New 100 Maths Lessons Year 4*. As teachers plan their work on a week-by-week basis, so the homework activities can be chosen to fit the appropriate unit of work. They may equally be used alongside the appropriate NNS units, as clearly indicated in the Teacher's notes at the beginning of each term.

For assessment, there are activities to support the 'Assessment lessons' built into the NNS medium-term plan, for example weeks 7 and 14 in the autumn term of Year 4. The assessment tasks are built around the key objectives taught during the preceding half-term and all objectives taught are covered in the appropriate assessment. Further information about using the assessment activities can be found on page 84.

Homework diary

Name of activity & date sent home	Child's comments		Helper's comments	Teacher's comments
	Write about what you enjoyed	Write about what you learned		

Activity name	Learning objectives	Content of homework	Managing the homework	All New 100 Maths Lessons Year 4	
				NNS	Page
The great estimation challenge!	• Make and justify estimates up to about 250.	**Puzzles to do at home** The children estimate some common household things but do not count them. The emphasis is on the process.	**Before:** Discuss the vocabulary of estimation and what it is used for. **After:** Ask the children to read out some of their estimates and discuss what strategies (if any) they used.	1	9
Make it four!	• Identify near doubles, using known doubles.	**Maths to share** Doubles game to be played with a helper.	**Before:** Give out the sheet and briefly explain the rules. **After:** Talk to the children about numbers they found hard to double.	2	14
Money, money, money!	• **Choose and use appropriate number operations and appropriate ways of calculating (mental, mental with jottings, pencil and paper) to solve problems.**	**Maths homework** Some short word problems for the children to solve.	**Before:** Explain that the children cannot use a calculator for these problems and that they should write down how they did them. **After:** Ask the children what methods they used to solve the problems.	2	15
Adding	• Use informal pencil-and-paper methods to support, record or explain additions and subtractions.	**Maths to share** The aim of this sheet is to encourage the children to share their calculation methods with someone at home.	**Before:** Remind the children how to set out a vertical addition question, and to add the most significant digits first. **After:** Work through the examples together, and invite children from each ability group to show the others by writing on the board how they worked out an answer.	3	23
Small number add	• Add three or four small numbers, finding pairs totalling 10, or 9 or 11.	**Maths to share** Children choose three or four small numbers and add them, then explain to the helper the strategy they used.	**Before:** Review the strategies the children might use for adding three or four small numbers. **After:** Invite children from each ability group to read out one of their additions for the others to total mentally. Discuss the strategy chosen and why it was appropriate.	3	23

Activity name	Learning objectives	Content of homework	Managing the homework	All New 100 Maths Lessons Year 4	
				NNS	Page
Polygon search	• **Classify polygons using criteria such as number of right angles, whether or not they are regular, symmetry properties.**	**Maths to share** A sheet that encourages children to find polygons at home.	**Before:** Remind the children of the definition of a polygon: a closed shape with three or more sides. **After:** Ask the children what shapes they found and what properties they have. If the children found unusual shapes they might enjoy searching on the internet to find out their names.	4	29
Converting lengths	• Use, read and write standard metric units (km, m, cm, mm), including their abbreviations.	**Maths homework** Some metric conversions for the children to practise.	**Before:** Ask the children how many mm in a cm, cm in a metre etc. **After:** Review the sheet together. Invite some children from each ability group to suggest answers.	5	34
What will you choose?	• Suggest suitable units and measuring equipment to estimate or measure length.	**Maths to share** Children suggest what equipment to use, and units, to measure given items.	**Before:** Ask questions such as: *How would you measure the length of the floor? What units would you use?* **After:** Review the sheet together. Discuss suggestions that children make for measuring equipment and units.	5	34
The shortest distance	• Measure and calculate the perimeter of rectangles and simple shapes.	**Maths homework** The children find the shortest distance across a grid.	**Before:** Review how to change mm to cm, cm to m. **After:** Invite solutions from children from each ability group. Discuss how the children totalled the measurements.	6	41
Find the treasure	• Recognise positions and directions: for example, describe and find the position of a point on a grid of squares where the lines are numbered.	**Puzzles to do at home** The children record given coordinates to find the treasure, then make up a similar puzzle for their helper to try.	**Before:** Review how to read and record coordinates. **After:** invite children from each group to set their hidden treasure puzzle for the others to solve..	6	42
All change!	• Count on or back in tens, hundreds or thousands from any whole number up to 10,000.	**Maths homework** Children count on and back from 100 in steps of the same size. They record the sequence of numbers.	**Before:** Count together in 7s from 100 for ten steps. Then count back in 7s from 100. **After:** Invite children from each group to read out one of their solutions. The other children can quietly join in with the number sequence.	8	44

Activity name	Learning objectives	Content of homework	Managing the homework	All New 100 Maths Lessons Year 4	
				NNS	Page
Sums and products	• Solve mathematical problems or puzzles, recognise and explain patterns and relationships, generalise and predict. Suggest extensions by asking 'What if....?'	**Puzzles to do at home** The children find pairs of numbers that give a specific sum and product.	**Before:** Ask the children to say which two numbers have the sum of 15 and the product of 50 (5, 10). Ask them to explain how they worked this out. **After:** Invite solutions from children from each ability group. Ask the children to explain how they solved the problems.	**8**	**47**
Multiplication and division practice	• Develop and refine written methods for TU x U, TU ÷ U. • Check with an equivalent calculation.	**Maths to share** Four questions involving multiplication and division, to be discussed with a helper.	**Before:** Review multiplication and division written methods. **After:** Invite a child from each ability group to explain, writing on the board how they found the solutions.	**9**	**53**
Times-tables challenge	• **Know by heart multiplication facts for 2, 3, 4, 5 and 10 times-tables.**	**Homework activity** The child is timed as he or she works through a grid of answers to tables facts.	**Before:** Practise reciting the table facts. Ask questions such as: *What is 6 x 5? What is 24 ÷ 3?* **After:** Use the grid during a Starter. Challenge the children to write a fact for each number as you call it out. Keep the pace sharp.	**9**	**53**
Missing signs	• **Choose and use appropriate number operations and appropriate ways of calculating (mental, mental with jottings, pencil and paper) to solve problems.**	**Puzzles to do at home** There are missing signs in some number sentences for the children to complete.	**Before:** Write an example on the board such as 60 □ 5 = 12, and ask the children to explain what sort of number sentence they think it is, and why. **After:** Review the work together. Invite the children to explain how they solved the problems.	**10**	**57**
Fraction shapes	• **Recognise mixed numbers,** such as 5¾.	**Maths homework** Children find the fraction that a smaller shape is of a larger one.	**Before:** Draw on the board a row of two squares, then another row of eight squares and ask the children to say the relationship of the smaller row to the larger. **After:** If the children have made some more fraction shape puzzles, invite them to draw these on the board for other children to try.	**11**	**64**

Teacher's notes

Activity name	Learning objectives	Content of homework	Managing the homework	All New 100 Maths Lessons Year 4	
				NNS	**Page**
Fraction pelmanism	• **Recognise the equivalence of simple fractions** (e.g. fractions equivalent to ½, ¼ or ¾).	**Maths to share** An equivalence game to play.	**Before:** Review equivalence of the fractions on the sheet. Ask the children to say the equivalences. **After:** The children can play this as a game of Snap. Divide the class into two teams with captains. Turn over two cards each time. The first captain to say Snap, encouraged by the team, wins those cards.	**11**	**66**
Counting on	• **Develop and refine written methods for column subtraction of two whole numbers less than 1000.**	**Maths homework** Children practise using the counting-on method to solve some subtraction questions.	**Before:** Review using the counting-on method for subtraction. **After:** Invite children from each group to explain, using the board, how they worked out the answers to one question.	**12**	**74**
Time snap	• Use am and pm and the notation 9: 53.	**Maths to share** Children take home some 'Time pelmanism' cards and play Snap, matching the times.	**Before:** Review reading times from analogue and digital clocks to the nearest minute. **After:** Play the Snap game with the class in two teams. It would be helpful to use an enlarged set of cards for this.	**12**	**75**
Card connect	• **Use known number facts and place value to add or subtract mentally, including any pair of two-digit whole numbers.**	**Maths to share** A 'Follow me' card activity.	**Before:** Ask the children some two-digit addition and subtraction questions. Review with them how they found the answers. **After:** Use the activity again as part of a Starter. Encourage the children to complete it as quickly as they can.	**13**	**79**
Times-tables practice	• **Know by heart multiplication facts for 2, 3, 4, 5 and 10 times-tables.**	**Maths homework** The children write a table fact for each of ten of the numbers in a grid. The table contains two numbers that do not appear in the tables.	**Before:** Recite the tables quickly together. Remind the children that if they are not sure about a number this is one way to check which table it appears in. **After:** Discuss how the children worked out which numbers did not belong in the tables. They may point out that both numbers are odd. (Both are prime.)	**13**	**82**

Name Date

The great estimation challenge!

- See if you can find some of the containers listed in the table below.
- Estimate how many things are in each container.
- Make sure your helper knows what you are doing and do not open any packet you should not!
- Explain how you made your estimate.

Things in containers	Estimate	How I made my estimate
Packet of cereal		
Packet of pasta		
Can of beans or peas		
Potatoes in a bag		
Biscuits in a packet/tin		
Sweets in a bag		

- Talk to someone at home about your estimates. What do they think about your estimates? Are they too high? Too low? About right?
- Find something of your own at home to estimate. Record it in this table.

Item	Estimate

Dear Helper

This activity is aimed at improving your child's estimation skills. For this sheet the exact answer is not important. Try to encourage your child to think of ways of estimating that are not just wild guesses. An estimate is really an informed guess. If your child is stuck, first suggest something like working out how many cornflakes fit on a spoon. Ask: *How many spoonfuls might be in the packet?* Challenge your child to make larger estimates, such as: *How many bricks were used to build this house?* Ask them to work out a way of making this very large estimate.

Name Date

Make it four!

- You will need counters or something similar to play this game. 1p and 5p coins are ideal but do give them back when you've finished!
- Take turns to point to a number in the top grid, like 41, and say, 'I can get double 41 by doubling 40 (pointing to that number in the bottom grid) and adding 2.'
- If your helper agrees the answer is correct, you can cover the number in the top grid and the one in the bottom grid with your counters.
- The winner is the first person to cover four squares in the top grid. You can't reuse numbers that are covered in the bottom grid.

29	38	41	59	61	9
22	57	53	39	82	19
81	99	21	18	49	91
43	89	11	31	92	51

100	80	36	120	160	100
120	60	40	180	60	120
40	80	80	20	180	100
20	180	60	100	20	40

Dear Helper

The process of doubling the numbers in the top grid is called using 'near doubles'. Each one is near a number that is easier to double, so we can do that and adjust the answer. An understanding of doubles is very important for children, as is an understanding of these near doubles. For example, double 42 is the same as 42 + 42, which is easier as double 40 and add on 4. Alternatively, to add 38 + 38, double 40 and subtract 4. If your child is unsure about how to calculate near doubles, encourage them to use paper-and-pencil methods to help. Challenge your child to work mentally to find the near doubles.

Name Date

Money, money, money!

■ Use any method you like (but not a calculator) to answer these questions. Show your workings.

1. A CD costs £9.99. Sundeep gets 50p a week for pocket money. How many weeks will it take Sundeep to save enough money to buy a CD?

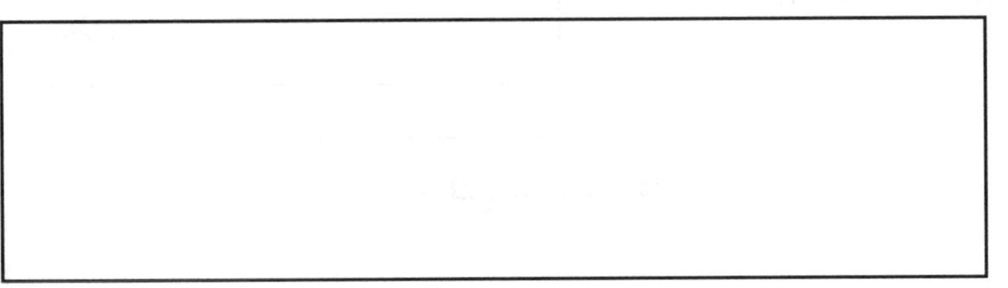

2. It costs £1.20 for a child to go to the cinema. How much will it cost for six children to go to the cinema?

3. When I went shopping last week I bought three books. Each book cost £5.99. How much change did I get from £20?

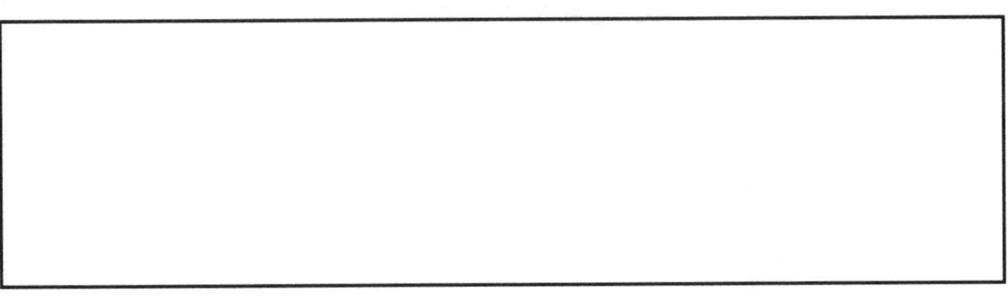

4. A large fruit bar costs 65p. How many bars could I buy if I had £3?

Dear Helper
Solving problems is a very important part of mathematics. Talk to your child about the problems above. Ask whether they need to use +, –, × or ÷ each time. Allow them to solve the problems in any way they see fit. Try to resist the temptation to tell them a 'quicker' way! If your child is really stuck let them use the calculator, but ask them to write down which keys they press.

Name Date

Adding

- Do these sums two ways.
  - Work horizontally. Show your workings.
  - Write the sum vertically. Show your workings.
  - Share your work with a helper.

37 + 63 = 90 + 10 = 100

```
  37
+ 63
  90
+ 10
 100
```

1. 65 + 45 =

2. 83 + 89 =

3. 123 + 45 =

4. 246 + 78 =

Dear Helper
Your child has been taught a method for working out addition. Listen to your child explain how they have worked out the answer. Try not to be tempted to teach your child a 'quicker' way as this method is part of the National Numeracy Strategy. If your child struggles with these questions, suggest that they work horizontally only. They can add the hundreds, then the tens, then the units, and finally total all of these. (You probably learned to add starting with the units.) Challenge your child with an example such as 357 + 246 (500 + 90 + 13 = 603).

Name Date

Small number add

- You will need four coins or counters.
- Make your own 1–9 number cards or number grid.
  - Toss the coins onto your number cards or grid.
  - Write down the numbers that the coins land on in the addition sentence below.
  - Decide how to total the numbers using a mental strategy.
  - Write down the answer.
- Do this five more times.

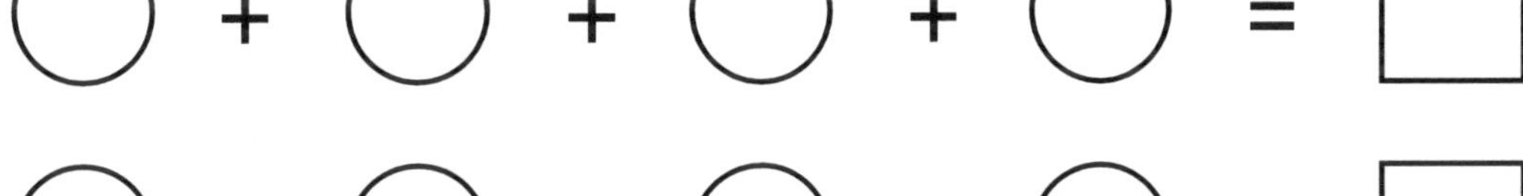

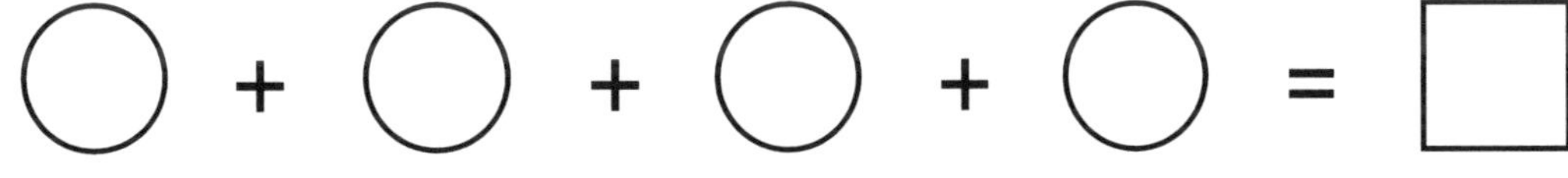

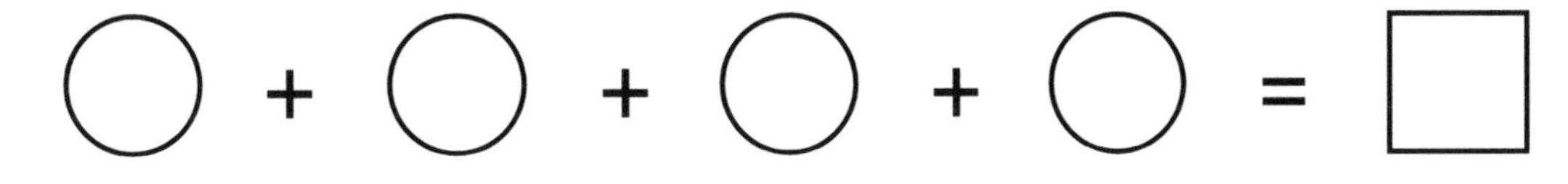

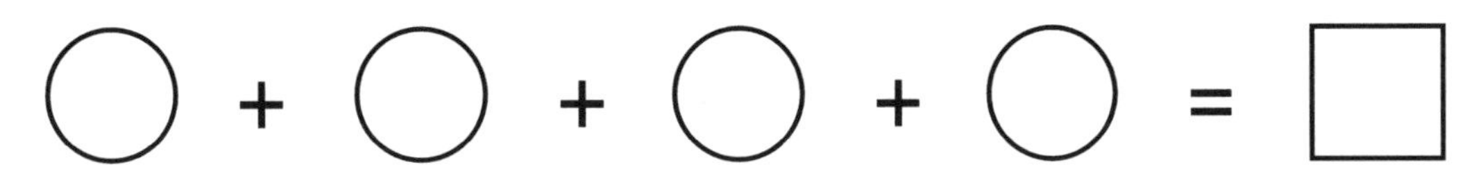

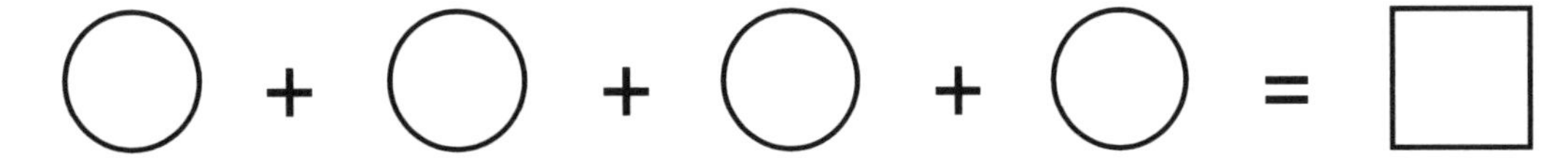

○ + ○ + ○ + ○ = □

Dear Helper

This activity helps your child to practise using the addition strategies of: making a 10 first; starting with the largest number; finding numbers that total 9 or 11 by adding 10 and adjusting by 1. As your child finds each total, encourage them to explain which strategy they chose and to explain how they used it. If your child finds the activity difficult, work together and discuss how each set of four numbers could be totalled. Challenge your child to add three more cards to their set or an extra row to their grid showing the numbers 11, 13 and 15. Suggest that they do a further three examples that they can write on the back of this sheet.

Name Date

Polygon search

- Look around you at home with a helper.
- Find as many different polygons as you can.
  - Draw them in the recording box.
  - Write the name of the polygon underneath its picture.

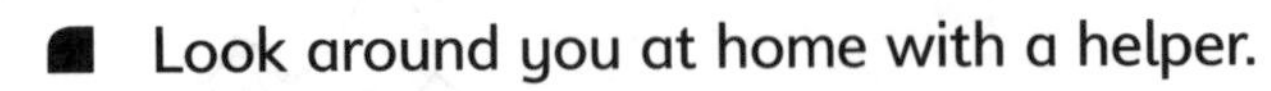

Dear Helper
This activity will help your child to recognise and name polygons. Polygon is another word for a flat shape that has three or more sides with no gaps between them. If your child finds this difficult, look around the house together. Children might spot windows, television screens, books, all of which have one face which is a rectangle. Challenge your child to find more unusual shapes and, where they do not know the name of the shape, write underneath how many sides it has.

Name Date

Converting lengths

- Complete this chart.

☐ millimetres = 1 centimetre

☐ centimetres = 1 metre

☐ metres = 1 kilometre

- Write the lengths in the new units.

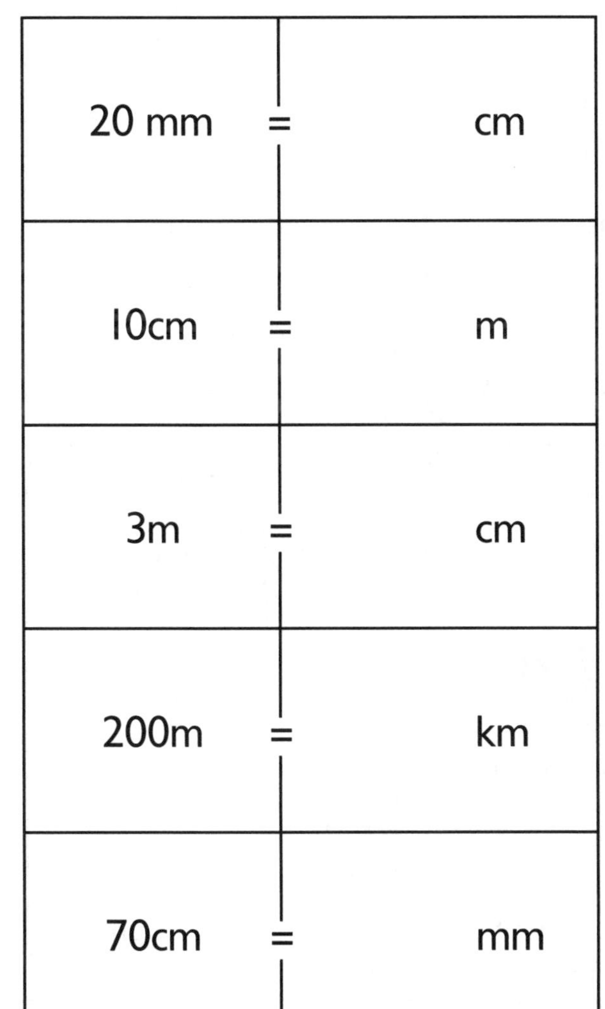

20 mm	=	cm	45cm	=	mm
10cm	=	m	6km	=	m
3m	=	cm	8m	=	cm
200m	=	km	400mm	=	cm
70cm	=	mm	350cm	=	m

Dear Helper

This activity gives your child practice in converting length measurements into different units. If your child finds this difficult, talk together about how many of one unit there are in the other. The chart at the top will help with this. Challenge your child to write some conversions for more complicated measures, such as 956cm into metres (9.56m), and so on.

Name Date

What will you choose?

- Look at each picture.
  - Imagine that you have to measure what is in the picture.
  - Write underneath which measuring equipment you would choose (ruler, metre stick or measuring tape).
  - Write which units you would choose.

I would measure this with a ______________

I would use ______________ units.

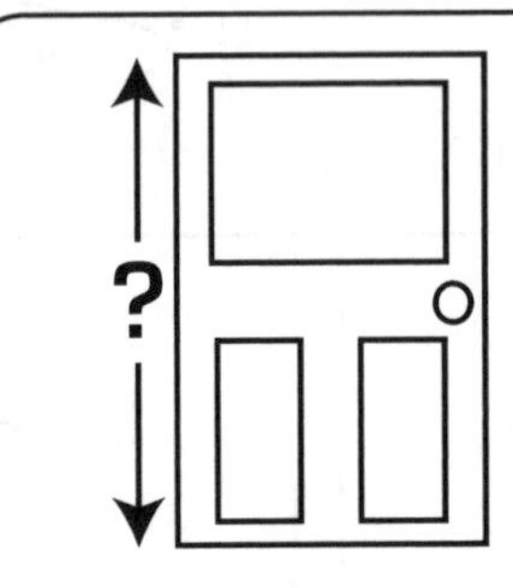

I would measure this with a ______________

I would use ______________ units.

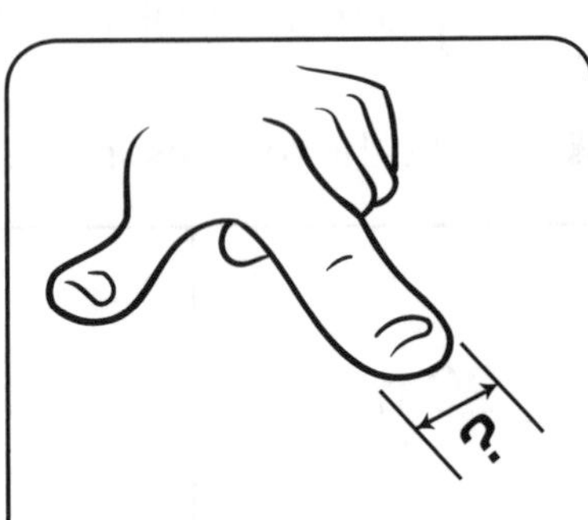

I would measure this with a ______________

I would use ______________ units.

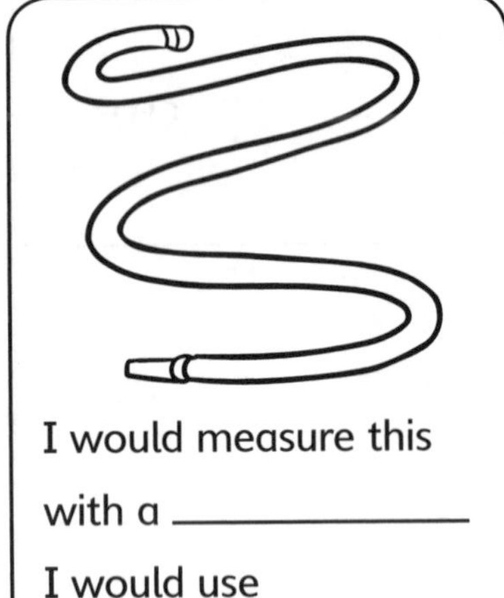

I would measure this with a ______________

I would use ______________ units.

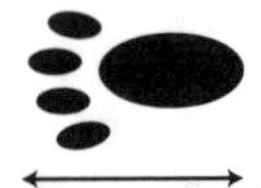

I would measure this with a ______________

I would use ______________ units.

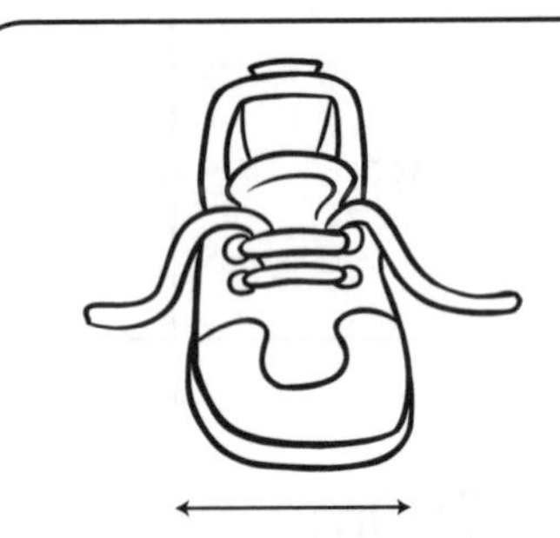

I would measure this with a ______________

I would use ______________ units.

Dear Helper

This activity helps your child to remember that the range of measuring equipment has different uses, and that the appropriate standard units need to be chosen for the size of what is measured. If your child is unsure about which units to use, discuss the size of a unit. Your child can then make a good estimate of which to choose. Challenge your child to think of more things that could be measured for length, what to measure them with, and the units to use. They could write this on the back of this sheet.

Name Date

The shortest distance

- Find the shortest distance across this grid.
- You may move horizontally or vertically.

Start

120cm	8m	2m	500cm	24m
400cm	1.5m	17m	420cm	345cm
40mm	56cm	184cm	12.5m	320cm

Finish

Dear Helper
This activity helps your child to total measurements. These measurements are in different units, so it would be helpful to change these into the same unit where possible. If your child finds this difficult, do this together, discussing how many millimetres make a centimetre, and so on. Challenge your child to find the longest route. They may use a calculator if they wish.

Name Date

Find the treasure

- Plot these points on the grid:

  (5, 1) (5, 5) (1, 1) (1, 5)

  - ☐ Join the points.
  - ☐ Now join the diagonals.
  - ☐ The treasure is hidden where the diagonals cross.
  - ☐ Write the coordinates of the treasure.

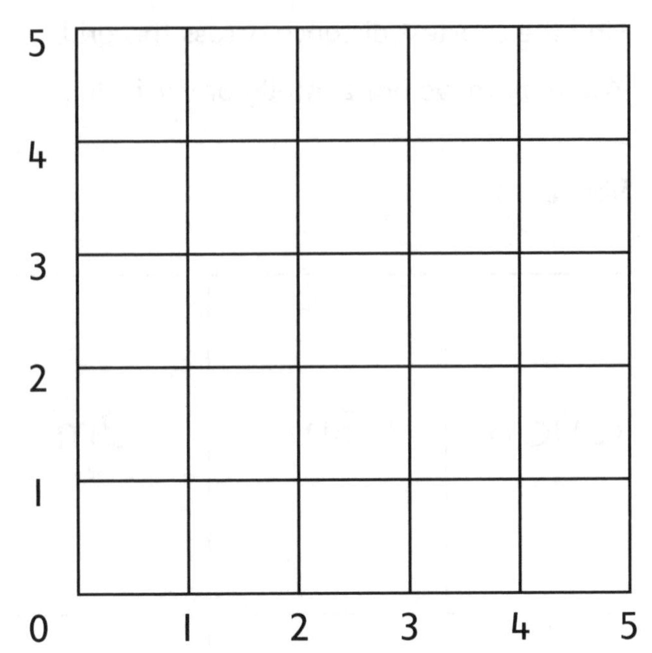

- Now make up your own hidden treasure coordinates.
- Challenge your helper to find the treasure.

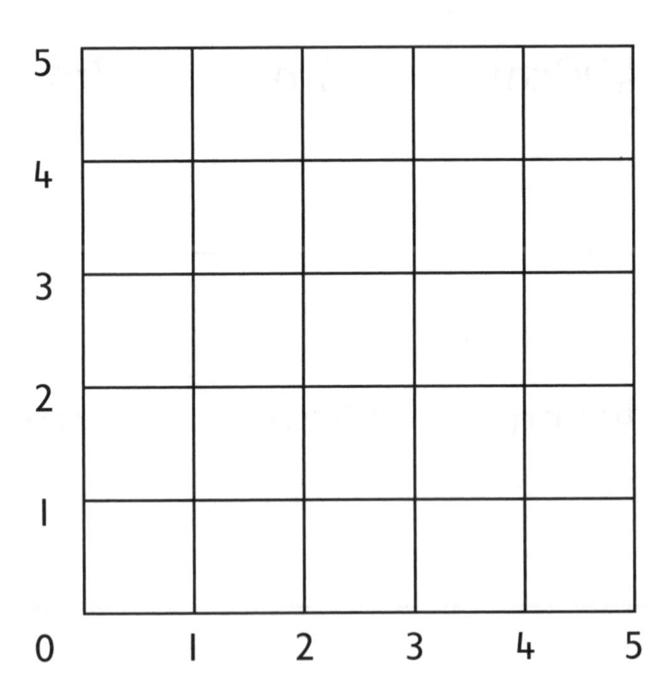

Dear Helper

This activity helps your child to read and plot coordinates. The first number is on the horizontal side of the grid, and the second number is on the vertical side of the grid. If your child finds this hard, ask them to point to each number, then to find where the horizontal and vertical lines meet. This will give the point on the grid. Challenge your child to make up a more complex puzzle for you to solve.

Name Date

All change!

56

- You will need a counter or coin.
- Begin with 56.
  - ☐ Toss a counter onto the number grid below.
  - ☐ Add the counter number to 56 again and again, at least five times. Write the sequence of numbers on the back of the sheet.
  - ☐ Make ten number sequences by adding.
  - ☐ Now, subtract the counter number from 100 five times.
  - ☐ Write the sequence of numbers on the back of the sheet.
  - ☐ Make ten number sequences by subtracting.

2	8	10	17
4	16	13	10
11	9	6	12
7	3	14	5

Dear Helper

This activity helps your child to count on and back in steps of the same size. If they find this difficult, say the start number together, then ask them to add on the counter number. Write down the answer, add again, and so on. For some numbers your child may spot a pattern. For example, add 9 gives 56, 65, 74 and so on – where the tens digit increases by 1 each time while the units digit decreases by 1. Challenge your child to write the sequence of numbers for each of the numbers in the grid.

Name Date

Sums and products

- Solve these problems.
  - Write your answer.
  - Write a sentence to show how you worked it out.

What numbers have a sum of 14 and a product of 48? ____________________

What numbers have a sum of 16 and a product of 63? ____________________

What numbers have a sum of 10 and a product of 25? ____________________

What numbers have a sum of 11 and a product of 24? ____________________

What numbers have a sum of 13 and a product of 42? ____________________

What numbers have a sum of 13 and a product of 36? ____________________

- Make up a number problem like these.
  - Write it on the back of this sheet.
  - Now ask your helper or a friend to solve it!

Dear Helper

Children tend to make up very hard problems when challenging adults, so it's OK to ask the child to show you how to solve their number problem. Make sure your child brings their number problem back to school for their friends to try in class.

Name Date

Multiplication and division practice

- Use the way you have been shown at school to do these problems.
- Explain to your helper what you are doing.

56 × 7 =	83 × 5 =
35 ÷ 5 =	72 ÷ 6 =

Dear Helper
Your child has been doing multiplication and division problems at school. They have been learning ways to do them that you will probably not have seen before. Ask your child to explain how they have found the answers. Try not to show them a method that you think might be quicker because the method that your child is using is the recommended method of the National Numeracy Strategy. Ask your child to explain, for each question, what they are doing and why, and how they have found the answer.

Name Date

Times-tables challenge

- Ask your helper to time you and check your multiplication or division as you play this game.
  - Choose a square along the start row and say a multiplication or division fact for the number on that square. For example: $5 \times 4 = 20$.
  - Now move to a square in the next row that touches your previous square (for example: 8 or 44).
  - Say a multiplication or division fact for the number on that square.
  - Repeat this, moving from one square to a touching square in the next row until you reach the finish row.
- How long did this take you?
- Repeat the game, this time trying a different route across the grid.

Start	20	33	16	15	12	50
	8	44	21	70	6	25
	55	30	70	32	45	36
	28	80	16	48	2	90
	35	4	3	27	40	9
Finish	24	14	60	8	100	18

Dear Helper
Your child is expected to remember multiplication facts for the 2, 3, 4, 5 and 10 time-tables. This activity encourages them to practise recall of those facts. For example, if your child begins on 15, they might say $3 \times 5 = 15$, $5 \times 3 = 15$, $15 \div 3 = 5$ or $15 \div 5 = 3$. Timing your child will help them to realise how well they know these facts. If your child does not know one of the facts, talk about which multiplication table it is likely to come in, and why. Then ask them to say that table until they come to the fact. Challenge your child to see how quickly they can work through all the squares in the grid, and say a fact.

Name Date

Missing signs

- There are missing signs in these number sentences.
- Write in the signs so that the number sentence is true.

14 ☐ 28= 42

100 ☐ 23 = 77

23 ☐ 6= 138

102 ☐ 45 = 57

84 ☐ 6 = 14

Dear Helper
This activity helps your child to consider which number operation – addition, subtraction, multiplication or division – has been carried out to find the answer in these number sentences. Remind them that they must check that the sign works. If your child finds this difficult, talk through whether the answer is larger or smaller than the other numbers, and how much larger or smaller (if it is much larger it is probably multiplication; much smaller is probably division). Challenge your child to write some more questions like these to take back to school.

Name Date

Fraction shapes

■ Write what fraction the smaller shape is of the larger shape.

Dear Helper

This activity helps your child to recognise fractions of shapes (how much part of a shape is of the whole shape). If your child is uncertain about the fractions, suggest that they cut out the smaller part and place it over the whole so that they can make a direct comparison. Challenge your child to draw some more of these fraction shapes to try out on a friend.

Fraction pelmanism

- Play this game with a friend.
  - Cut out the cards.
  - Shuffle them.
  - Turn the cards face down on the table.
  - Take turns to pick up two cards.
  - If the two cards are equivalent you keep them.
  - The player to collect the most cards wins.

$\frac{1}{2}$	$\frac{2}{4}$	$\frac{3}{6}$	$\frac{5}{10}$	$\frac{4}{8}$	$\frac{10}{30}$
$\frac{1}{4}$	$\frac{2}{8}$	$\frac{4}{16}$	$\frac{6}{24}$	$\frac{20}{40}$	$\frac{4}{12}$
$\frac{1}{3}$	$\frac{3}{9}$	$\frac{1}{10}$	$\frac{2}{20}$	$\frac{4}{20}$	$\frac{3}{30}$
$\frac{3}{4}$	$\frac{6}{8}$	$\frac{8}{12}$	$\frac{50}{100}$	$\frac{6}{12}$	$\frac{75}{100}$

Dear Helper
This activity helps your child to recognise equivalent fractions, such as $\frac{1}{2}$, $\frac{2}{4}$, $\frac{4}{8}$. Play this game together. If your child does not recognise what the simplest form of the fraction is (for example, that $\frac{50}{100}$ is also $\frac{1}{2}$), discuss what the fraction says. For example, $\frac{8}{12}$ can be said as '8 pieces out of 12'. Talk about how this is the same as 4 out of 6 or 2 out of 3. Challenge your child to say the simplest equivalent form for all the cards.

Name Date

Counting on

- Practise subtracting numbers using the counting-on method.
- Explain to your helper how you worked out each one.
- Here is an example to remind you:

```
  345
 - 76
    4 to make 80
   20 to make 100
  200 to make 300
   40 to make 340
    5 to make 345
  269
```

1. 456 – 68 =

4. 991 – 76 =

2. 631 – 87 =

5. 436 – 77 =

3. 357 – 89 =

6. 841 – 75 =

Dear Helper
Your child has learned a new method of subtraction that involves 'counting on'. Ask your child to explain how this method works. If they find the method difficult, please do not teach an alternative one. The counting-on method is the one recommended by the National Numeracy Strategy, and is the one your child's school is teaching. Challenge your child to make up and try to solve some four-digit minus three-digit questions if they find the ones on this page easy, for example, 1527 – 315.

Name Date

Time snap

- Cut up the time pelmanism cards below, to make 20 separate cards.
- Play this game with a friend.
  - Shuffle the cards.
  - Place the cards in a stack, face down.
  - Take turns to turn over the top card.
  - Make two piles of turned-over cards.
  - When the top cards from each pile match, say 'Time snap!'
  - Whoever says this first, and is correct, takes the cards.
- The winner is the player with more cards when all the cards have been used.

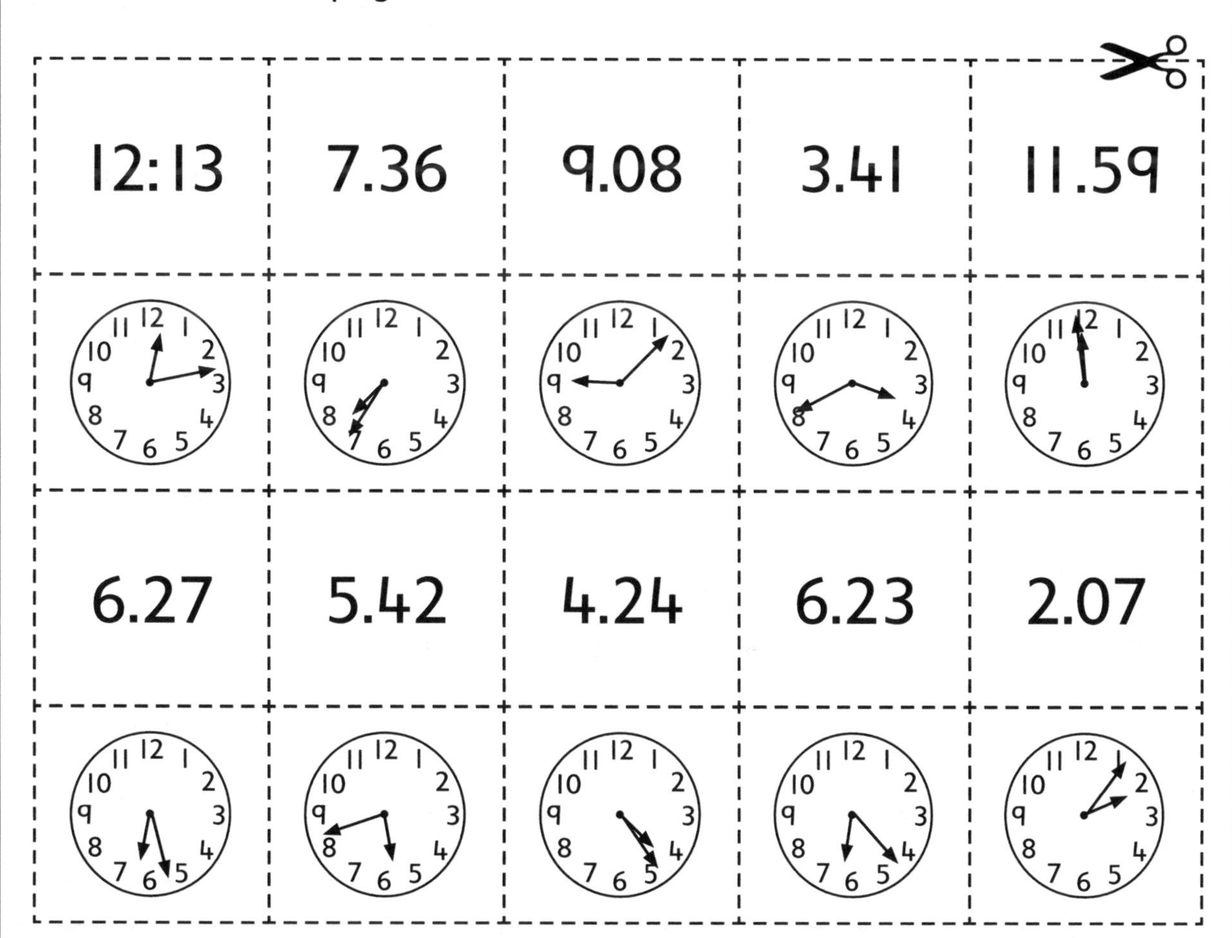

Dear Helper

This activity helps your child to read digital and analogue clock faces to the nearest minute. If your child struggles with this, spread the cards out, face up. Ask your child to find two cards that have matching times. Ask them to read the time from the cards. Challenge your child to tell the time at every opportunity, using both analogue and digital clocks around the house and when you are out.

Card connect

- Cut out the cards.
- Do this activity with a friend.
  - Put the cards out face up on the table.
  - One of you chooses a card and reads it out.
  - The other one finds the card that begins with the answer, then reads out that card.
  - Repeat this until all the cards have been used.

25 + 36	61 – 19	42 + 39	81 – 23	58 + 13
71 – 53	18 + 56	74 – 46	28 + 19	47 – 25
22 + 63	85 – 56	29 + 27	56 – 48	8 + 68
76 – 19	57 + 23	80 – 27	53 + 7	60 – 25
35 + 28	63 – 54	9 + 88	97 – 38	59 + 9
68 – 42	26 + 26	52 – 3	49 + 30	79 – 54

Dear Helper
This activity helps your child to add or subtract two two-digit numbers mentally. We have been playing it in class. Please do the activity together, taking turns to find the next card. If your child finds this difficult, show them the question on the card and ask them to add or subtract the tens, then the units. If this is still too difficult, ask your child to try a pencil-and-paper method. Challenge them to try the activity again, but time how long it takes to complete. How quickly can you do it together?

Name Date

Times-tables practice

- Look at the numbers in the grid.
- Choose a number and write its table fact. Work against the clock.
  - Be careful! There are 12 numbers, but two of them are not in the 2, 3, 4, 5 or 10 times–tables.
- Write the two numbers that are not in the tables in the boxes at the bottom of the sheet.

15	18	24
36	35	23
90	19	20
45	27	32

× =	× =
× =	× =
× =	× =
× =	× =
× =	× =

The two numbers that do not fit in the tables are: ☐ and ☐

Time taken: ____________

Dear Helper

Your child has been learning their 2, 3, 4, 5 and 10 times–tables at school. This activity will help your child to recall some of the facts. Please time how long it takes them to do this activity. If your child does not remember some of the facts, ask them to say the tables through and search for the fact. Remind them, though, that two numbers do not belong to the tables! Challenge your child to see for which numbers they can find more than one fact.

Teacher's notes

Activity name	Learning objectives	Content of homework	Managing the homework	All New 100 Maths Lessons Year 4	
				NNS	Page
'Less than' snap	• **Use symbols correctly, including less than (<), greater than (>), equals (=).**	**Maths to share** The children play a game with an adult. You might need to prepare some number cards from 1 to 30 for the children to take home.	**Before:** Demonstrate the game to the children. **After:** Ask if the children found any strategies to win.	1	87
Timed challenge	• **Use known number facts and place value to add or subtract mentally, including any pair of two-digit whole numbers.**	**Homework activity** Addition and subtraction questions to be read out by a helper and answered mentally or with rough jottings.	**Before:** Discuss methods that can be used. **After:** Ask individual children to tell you how long they took and go through any methods that helped them to solve each question.	2	93
The crossing-out challenge	• **Choose and use appropriate number operations and appropriate ways of calculating (mental, mental with jottings, paper and pencil) to solve problems.**	**Maths homework** Using the grid, children are asked to find and cross out numbers that satisfy different rules.	**Before:** Discuss an example and the vocabulary used. **After:** Go though individual examples and ask for other numbers that satisfy each rule.	3	96
Shopping trip	• Use addition/ subtraction operations to solve problems involving numbers in 'real life'.	**Puzzles to do at home** Children have to select as many items as they can from a post office that make exactly £2.50.	**Before:** Discuss the list of rules. **After:** Compare results. Who was able to buy the most items? Which items did they buy?	3	99
Estimating time	• Estimate and check times using seconds, minutes, hours.	**Puzzles to do at home** Children are asked to estimate how long it takes them to do various activities at home.	**Before:** Discuss how to estimate and time activities. **After:** Compare times and differences between estimates and real time.	4	102

Activity name	Learning objectives	Content of homework	Managing the homework	All New 100 Maths Lessons Year 4	
				NNS	Page
Estimating and measuring mass	• Suggest suitable units and equipment to estimate or measure mass.	**Puzzles to do at home** Children are asked to estimate masses and collect labels from food packets showing mass.	**Before:** Discuss what sorts of packets would be suitable to measure and bring in, and how to use scales at home. **After:** What types of scales did they find at home? Look at packaging: *Is the mass clearly displayed?*	4	103
Range of numbers	• **Choose and use appropriate number operations and appropriate ways of calculating (mental, mental with jottings, paper and pencil) to solve problems.**	**Puzzles to do at home** Children are asked to think of ten different number sentences using a range of numbers and all four operations.	**Before:** Talk through the examples given on the sheet. **After:** Share the number sentences as a class. Ask: *What did you notice about the range of numbers given?*	5	108
Colour by numbers	• Begin to know multiplication facts for 6, 7, 8 and 9 times-tables.	**Puzzles to do at home** Children are asked to colour-code numbers on a grid according to the times-table. They then have some questions to answer.	**Before:** Talk through the method for colour coding. It may be an idea to ask the children to make a list of all the numbers in the times-table. **After:** Talk through the questions at the end of the sheet.	5	112
Shapes and coordinates	• Recognise positions and directions: for example, describe and find the position of a point on a grid of squares where the lines are numbered.	**Maths homework** Children are asked to find the coordinates of squares and rectangles with particular areas and perimeters on a 5 × 5 grid square.	**Before:** Try the first question together to ensure that the children realise there are different answers that can all be correct. **After:** Share the different answers.	6	116
Angle grinding	• Begin to know that angles are measured in degrees and that one whole turn is 360° or four right angles.	**Puzzles to do at home** Children are asked to order angles of different sizes. They are then challenged to find examples of angles less than 90° at home.	**Before:** Talk through the numbering on the sheet. **After:** Go through the answers and share the locations of objects with angles less than 90°.	6	116

Activity name	Learning objectives	Content of homework	Managing the homework	All New 100 Maths Lessons Year 4	
				NNS	**Page**
Next in line	● Recognise and extend number sequences formed by counting from any number in steps of constant size, extending beyond zero when counting back.	**Maths to share** A game for two players to practise number sequences.	**Before:** Run through the rules of the game and trial the game if time is available. **After:** Go through the number sequences involved – in particular the 'add 25' sequence – and ask: *Who won?*	**8**	**119**
Times-tables investigation	● Make and investigate a general statement about familiar numbers by finding examples that satisfy it.	**Puzzles to do at home** Children are asked to investigate the statement 'a number in the 10 times-table must also be in the 2 and 5 times-tables'.	**Before:** Talk through how you would like the children to record their results. **After:** Ask: *Who thinks that the statement is true? Why?*	**8**	**120**
Remaining remainders	● **Find remainders after division.**	**Maths homework** Children are asked to answer a number of word problems involving dividing money and finding remainders.	**Before:** Ask the children to think of a suitable division problem involving remainders and to think about the number sentence related to the question. **After:** Talk through the answers and methods used to solve each one.	**9**	**126**
Certain about statements	● **Find remainders after division.**	**Puzzles to do at home** Children are asked to investigate remainders that can be made when you divide by 4.	**Before:** Explain that the work needs to be logical, and that if a remainder is greater than or equal to the divisor then it can be divided again. **After:** Ask: *Were the statements true? Why?*	**9**	**126**
Talk time	● **Choose and use appropriate number operations and ways of calculating (mental, mental with jottings, pencil and paper) to solve problems.**	**Maths homework** Children are asked to look at a telephone bill at home with an adult and work out an approximate charge for a call per minute.	**Before:** Talk about what to look for on a bill. Give an example of how to find the cost of the calls and then divide by the number of minutes. If you have time, prepare a 'pretend' phone bill to send home with the children, so that they all have the same answers to find. **After:** Compare costs and check answers.	**10**	**131**

Activity name	Learning objectives	Content of homework	Managing the homework	All New 100 Maths Lessons Year 4	
				NNS	Page
Close enough	• Choose and use appropriate number operations and ways of calculating (mental, mental with jottings, pencil and paper) to solve problems. • Approximate first.	**Maths homework** Children are given a series of calculations and suggestions of how to approximate the answers. They need to choose the best method and discuss this with an adult.	**Before:** Discuss rounding up and down to the nearest 10. **After:** Compare answers. Did everyone agree?	**10**	**131**
Focus on fractions	• **Recognise simple fractions that are several parts of a whole.**	**Puzzles to do at home** Children are asked to look at packets and recipe books at home to find as many examples of fractions used as they can.	**Before:** Talk about where children might look for examples at home. **After:** Discuss the various examples that the children bring in.	**11**	**137**
Equivalence snap	• **Recognise the equivalence of simple fractions.**	**Maths to share** Children are asked to play a game of 'snap' with an adult. When they see an equivalent fraction they say snap.	**Before:** Demonstrate the game to the children. **After:** Go through the answers and check children's understanding of equivalent fractions.	**11**	**138**
Favourite days	• Solve a problem by interpreting data in tables, charts, graphs and diagrams, for example bar charts with intervals labelled in 2s, 5s, 10s or 20s.	**Maths homework** Children are asked to answer some questions from a bar chart to show the most popular day of the school week.	**Before:** Discuss how to take readings from a bar chart. **After:** Compare answers. Discuss question 5: *Why do you think Wednesday could be a popular day of the week?* This cannot be established from the graph so children should guess, eg it could be a day for PE.	**12**	**142**

Name Date

'Less than' snap

- This is a game for two or more players.
- Prepare some cards displaying the numbers in the grid shown here:

1	2	3	4	5	6
7	8	9	21	22	23
24	25	26	27	28	29
41	42	43	44	54	67
89	121	134	155	143	117

- Instructions
  1. Write the numbers on card or paper. Cut them out and shuffle the cards.
  2. Deal the cards equally between the players.
  3. The first player puts two cards into the boxes below to make a correct number statement. For example, 2 < 11 (two *is less than* eleven).
  4. Players then take turns to place cards into the correct boxes, on top of the cards that are already there.
  5. If a player puts a card into an incorrect box, then she or he must pick up the pile.
  6. The winner is the first player to get rid of all their cards.
- When you have played the game once, repeat – but this time try to do it a little faster.

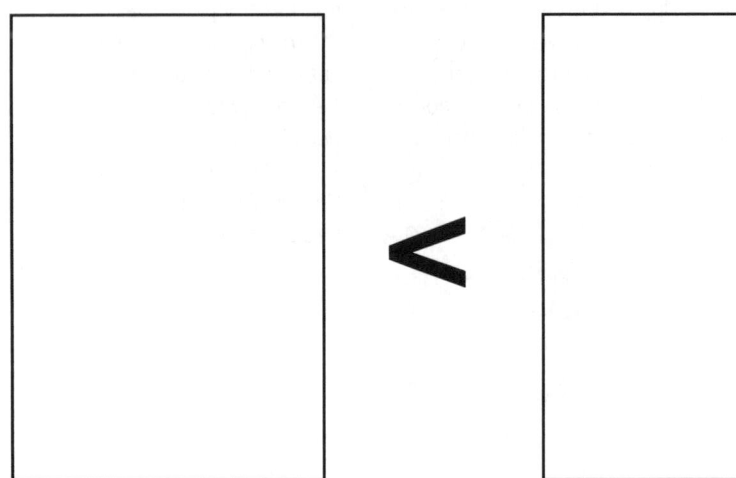

Dear Helper
This activity will reinforce the idea of 'greater than' and 'less than'. If your child is finding it difficult to place the cards on the correct pile, it may be helpful to draw crocodile teeth onto the inside edges of the 'less than' sign and say: *The crocodile always eats the larger number.* When your child places a card on a pile, encourage them to say, for example, *1 is less than 7*, or *7 is greater than 1*. For more of a challenge, prepare some cards with three-digit numbers, such as 543, 435 or 354.

Name Date

Timed challenge

- Work out these questions in your head, using the methods that you have learned this week.
- Think:
  - Can you make pairs of numbers that could help you?
  - Can you round the number up to the nearest 10 to help you?
  - Ask your helper to read out the following questions, and to time how long it takes you to answer the set of ten questions.

1. 23 + 17 = ______

2. 80 – 12 = ______

3. 29 + 11 = ______

4. 30 – 18 = ______

5. 47 – 18 = ______

6. 12 + 78 = ______

7. 100 – 34 = ______

8. 49 + 11 = ______

9. 17 + 4 = ______

10. 29 – 8 = ______

- How many did you get right?
- How long did it take you?

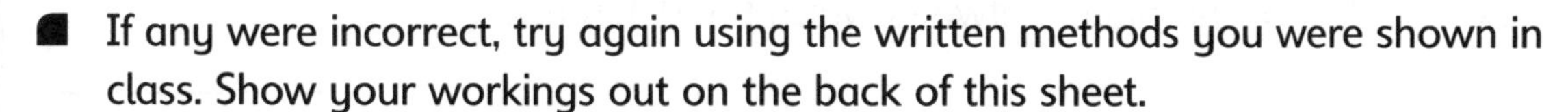

- If any were incorrect, try again using the written methods you were shown in class. Show your workings out on the back of this sheet.

Dear Helper
This activity will help your child to develop methods for adding and subtracting mentally. If your child is stuck, ask them to look at the last digits. With 23 + 17, for example, you can add together the 3 and the 7 to make 10, and then add 30. For subtraction, it may help to subtract the nearest multiple of 10, and then add on the difference. With 47 – 18, for example, work out 47 – 20, understand that you have subtracted 2 too many, and add that on at the end. It would be helpful, at the end of the timed activity, for you to go through the questions and ask: *How did you work that one out?* As a challenge you could try, with your child, to think of another way to get the same answer.

Name Date

The crossing-out challenge

9	76	99	75
33	1	63	69
73	79	43	14
52	27	19	50

- Cross out the number that is the sum of 6, 1 and 2. ______________
- Cross out the two numbers that have the largest difference. ______________
- Cross out the two numbers that have the smallest difference. ______________
- Cross out three pairs of numbers between which the difference is ten. ______________
- Cross out the number that is double seven. ______________
- Cross out the number that is half of 38. ______________
- Cross out the two numbers between which the difference is two. ______________
- Which number is left? ______________

Dear Helper

This activity will help your child to follow instructions and practise their calculation skills. Please make sure that your child follows the instructions in order and understand that once they have crossed out a number they cannot use that number again. Ask: *What does 'difference' mean?* (Take away.) *What does 'sum' mean?* (Add.) *What do we have to do when we double a number?* (Multiply by 2.) *How do we find half of a number?* (Divide by 2.) For a greater challenge, ask your child to make up another three sentences to describe a number in the grid.

Name Date

Shopping trip

- Look at the items available in Janni's local post office. She has £2.50 to spend.
- Work out what she could buy for her money. Stick to the following rules:
  - ☐ She may only buy one of each item.
  - ☐ She is aiming to buy as many items as possible.
  - ☐ She is aiming to have no change left over at the end.
- Show your working out on the back of this sheet.

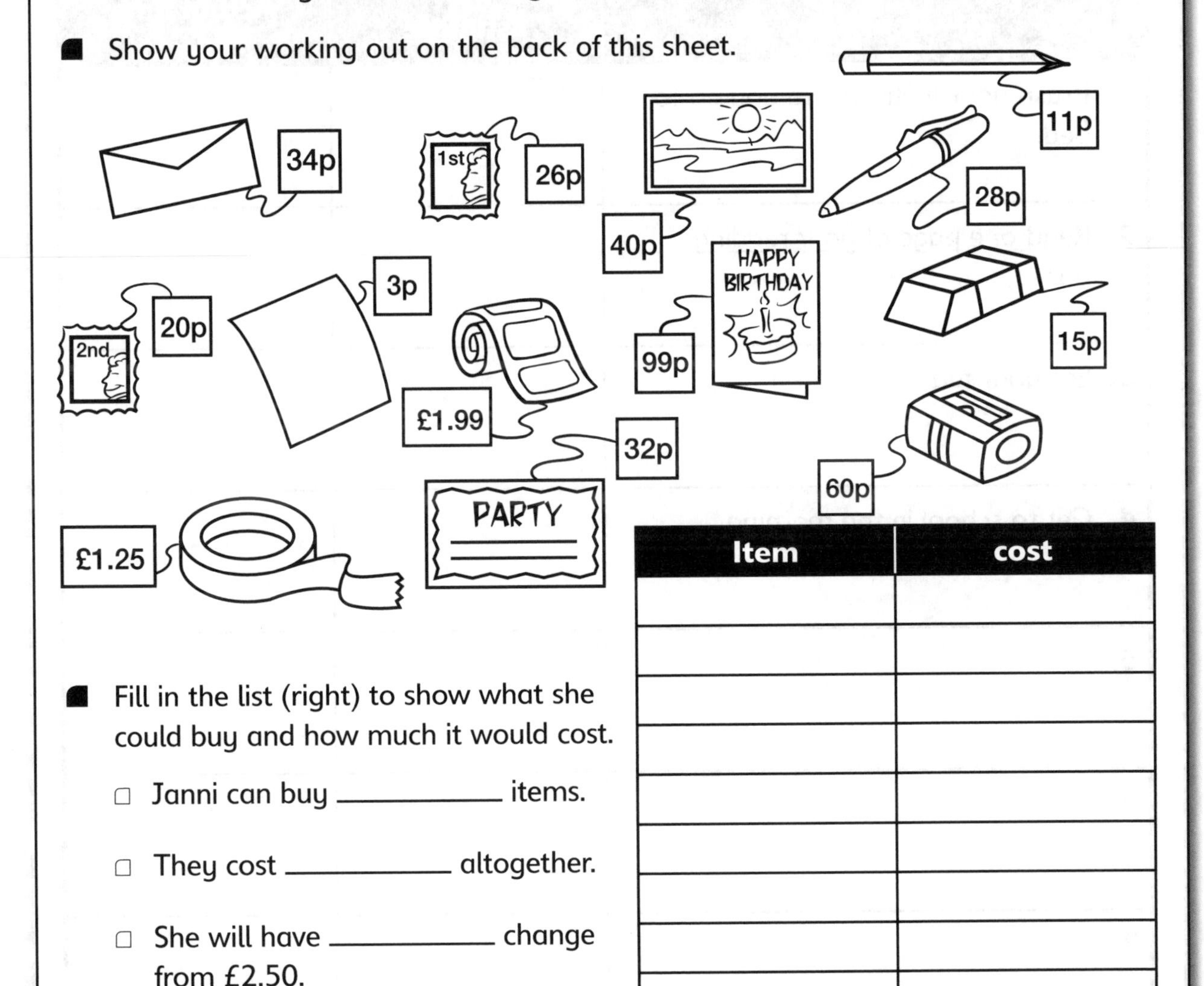

Item	cost

- Fill in the list (right) to show what she could buy and how much it would cost.
  - ☐ Janni can buy __________ items.
  - ☐ They cost __________ altogether.
  - ☐ She will have __________ change from £2.50.

Dear Helper
Encourage your child to add the amounts together mentally and then check their answers at the end. Less confident children can make a list (ensure that the units are lined up correctly) and then add up the columns, or find pairs of numbers that they are able to add and then find the sums of these pairs. As an extra challenge you could ask your child to find a different combination of things to buy. Ask: *How much change would you have left? Can you still buy the same number of items? What if you were allowed to buy more than one of each item?*

Name Date

Estimating time

- Estimate the time it takes to brush your teeth, then find out the actual time by timing yourself.
- Record the times in the table below. Do the same for the other activities listed. There are spaces left in the table for you to choose your own activities.

Activity	Estimate	Actual time taken
1. Brush your teeth before you go to bed.		
2. Read one page of your reading book.		
3. Eat your tea.		
4. Get to school in the morning.		
5.		
6.		
7.		

Dear Helper

Help your child to time the activities above using a stopwatch or clock. Together, look at the difference between the estimates and the actual times (in hours, minutes and seconds). For less confident children this activity could be timed over two nights – time the first night, then estimate and time the second night. As an extra challenge, your child could time these activities over a week and compare the times.

Name Date

Estimating and measuring mass

- Look at the following questions and circle the amounts that you think are correct.

1. How many letters would weigh approximately 100g?

1 2 5 10 20

2. How many sheets of A4 paper weigh approximately 100g?

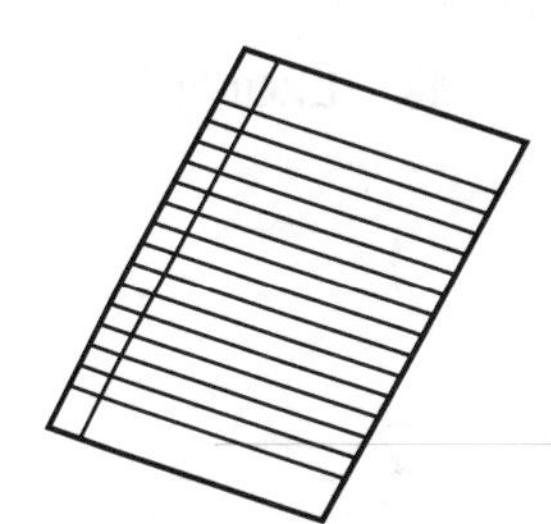

3 20 50 100 200

3. How many mugs weigh approximately 500g?

1 2 3 4 5

4. How many tablespoons weigh approximately 500g?

2 5 10 20 40

- Now look in your food cupboard to see if there are any packets with the mass marked on them. Look for a packet that weighs between 100 grams and 500 grams.
- Make a note of any you find, or take an empty packet to school to show your teacher.

Dear Helper

This activity will help your child to understand the relationship between different weights. They have been learning about grams and kilograms at school this week. To support your child, it may help to weigh one object using scales and then use that as a guide for other objects. If this is not possible, find an object that weighs 100g or 500g (a packet or tin that has the weight marked on it) and encourage your child to hold an object in one hand and try to compare it with the 100g or 500g weight in the other hand. As an extra challenge, ask: *How many would I need to make 1kg? ... 2kg? ... 5kg?*

Name Date

Range of numbers

- Use all four operations and the numbers below to make ten different calculations.
- The rule is that all answers must be between 50 and 100.

2 3 5 7 11 13 17 19 23 29

- Examples: $2 \times 29 = 58$ or $17 + 19 + 23 = 59$.

1. ______
2. ______
3. ______
4. ______
5. ______
6. ______
7. ______
8. ______
9. ______
10. ______

Dear Helper

This activity encourages your child to look at a range of numbers and make decisions about calculations. To support less confident children, decide on a starting number together and then use add (+) or multiply (×) in order to make a number larger. As an extra challenge, encourage your child to include five calculations using divide (÷) or multiply (×) as part of the sentence.

Name Date

Colour by numbers

- Using colouring pencils, follow the instructions below.
  - ☐ Colour in all the numbers in the 6 times-table red.
  - ☐ Colour in all the numbers in the 7 times-table blue.
  - ☐ Colour in all the numbers in the 8 times-table green.
  - ☐ Colour in all the numbers in the 9 times-table yellow.
  - ☐ If the number is not in the 6, 7, 8 or 9 times-table then leave it uncoloured.

6	7	8	9	10
16	17	45	19	20
26	27	28	29	30
35	37	38	39	40
14	21	12	49	50
2	57	58	59	60
66	32	64	69	70

- Now answer these questions:

1. Find the sum of all the numbers coloured red. ____________________

2. Find the difference between the largest number coloured green and the smallest number coloured green. __________

3. How many more blue numbers are there than yellow? ____________

Dear Helper
This activity will help your child revise the 6, 7, 8 and 9 times-tables. It may be helpful to ask your child to write down these tables in lists on another piece of paper before they start (1 × 7 = 7, 2 × 7 = 14, etc). As a challenge you could ask your child to look at the numbers not yet coloured in and ask: *Which numbers are even? Which times-table would they be in?* (2) *If we coloured in the even numbers, is there a times-table that would include most of the remaining numbers?*

Name Date

Shapes and coordinates

- Find the coordinates of mystery shapes. Read the clues carefully.
- Draw your shapes onto the grid and then write down the coordinates under the clue. (Remember to use brackets.)

1. I am a square with sides of length 4cm.

____

2. I am a rectangle with a perimeter of 20cm.

____

3. I am a rectangle with an area of 15cm^2.

____

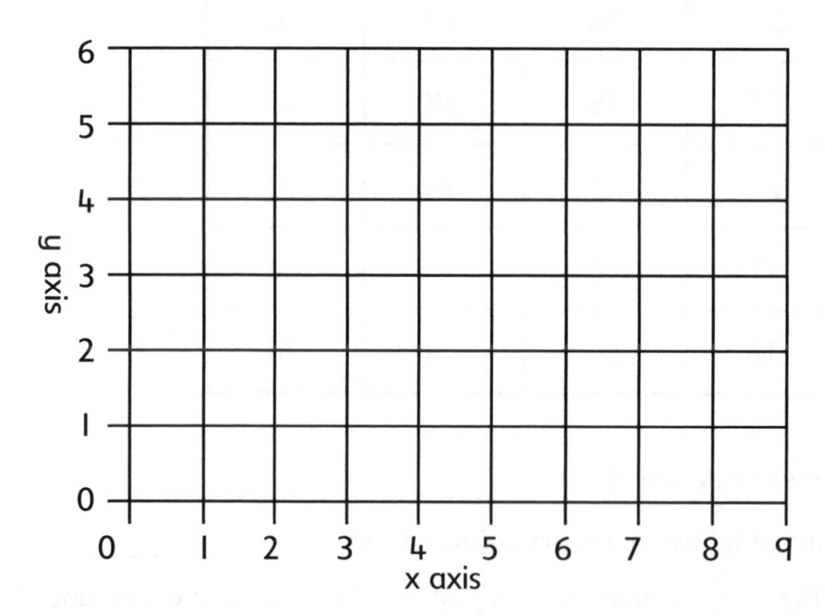

- Now make up a clue to another mystery shape that would fit onto the grid.
- Write the coordinates of the shape below, and remember what shape it is.

____

Dear Helper
Your child has been learning how each point on a grid of lines (a point is where the lines cross) can be referred to using numbers such as (2, 3). This is called a 'coordinate pair'. The first number means the number of lines along the grid, and the second number means the number of lines up the grid, so (1, 2) means '1 along and 2 up'. Remind your child that the perimeter is the distance all the way around a shape, and the area is the space inside a shape.

Name Date

Angle grinding

- Number the boxes 1 to 8 in order, starting with the smallest angle.

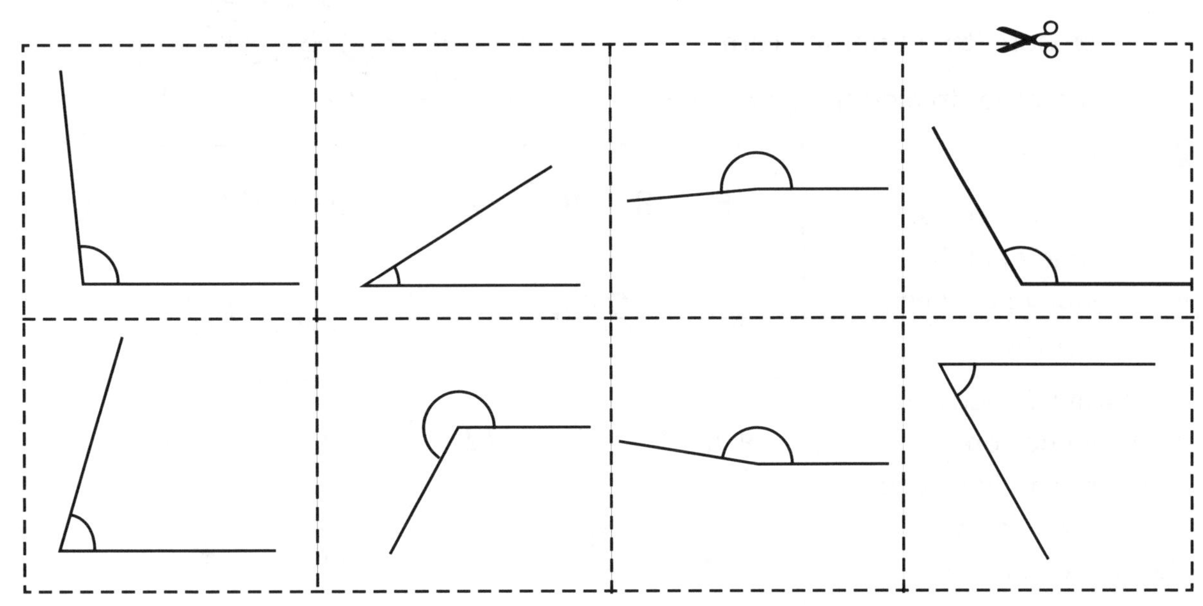

- Draw in an angle matching the descriptions in the boxes below.

A right angle	Half a right angle	Half of 360 degrees

- How would these fit into your ordered angles above?

- Challenge: How many angles can you find in your house that are less than 90 degrees? Write on the back of the sheet where you have spotted these.

Dear Helper

This activity revises what your child has learned about angles: that they are measured in degrees, that there are 360° in a full turn and 90° in a quarter turn or right angle. Ask: *Is this angle greater than or less than 90°?* When your child is looking for angles less than 90°, suggest that they use the corner of a piece of paper to compare the size of the angles. Angles less than 90° can be found on graters, knives, electrical plugs or on clocks. As an extra challenge, look at a clock together and ask: *At what times would there be an angle less than 90° between the hands?*

Name Date

Next in line

- For this game you will need:
  - ☐ scissors (to cut out the cards)
  - ☐ a partner to play the game with.

- Instructions

☐ Cut out the cards. Shuffle and deal the cards equally between the two players.

☐ **Player 1** reads out the sequence on the first card carefully, and repeats it if asked. **Player 2** must then say the next number in the sequence and explain the rule.

☐ If Player 2 is correct the card is placed face down on the table and Player 2 now reads one of her/his cards to Player 1. If the answer is incorrect or partly incorrect it stays in Player 1's hand.

☐ The winner is the first player to guess all the sequences in their opponent's hand.

16, 18, 20, 22 Answer: 24	100, 97, 94, 91 Answer: 88
45, 54, 63, 72 Answer: 81	34, 29, 24, 19 Answer: 14
1, 12, 23, 34, 45 Answer: 56	2, 27, 52, 77 Answer: 102
14, 20, 26, 32, 38 Answer: 44	80, 73, 66, 59, 52 Answer: 45
53, 45, 37, 29, Answer: 21	45, 58, 71, 84, 97 Answer: 110

Dear Helper

This game will help your child practise number sequences. Make sure that the children do not look at the answers as they are being cut out. Play the first game slowly, repeating the sequences twice, then reshuffle the cards and play a little faster. Each time ask: *What is the difference between the numbers? or What has been added/subtracted?* For extra support, ask your child to write down the sequence as it is being read out. As an extra challenge ask: *What would the next number in the sequence be? or What if we started with 99?*

Name Date

Times-tables investigation

- Investigate the following statement by trying out lots of examples to decide if it is true:
  - If a number is in the 10 times-table it is also in the 2 and the 5 times-tables.

- Complete this sentence (circle true or false).
  - I think the statement is true/false because:

Dear Helper
This homework aims to help your child investigate a general statement. They could start by writing out the 10 times-table and then write out the 2 and the 5 times-tables to compare them. Ask them to bring back to school everything they write down while working on this investigation. As a challenge you could ask your child to think up a similar statement about other times-tables, for example the 6, 3 and 2 times-tables.

Name Date

Remaining remainders

- Work out the following problems, showing all of your working out.

1. I saved some money for a computer game, which cost £45. I saved £4 a month. How long did it take me to save? How much did I have left over?

___

2. Books cost £5 in a sale. How many books can I buy with £24? How much will I have left?

___

3. Glue is packed in packs of two tubes. How many packs would I need for 35 tubes of glue?

___

4. Chairs are stacked in piles of ten. How many piles will I need for 54 chairs? How many extra chairs will I have?

___

5. Tins are sold in packs of four. If I want 23 tins, how many packs of four must I buy and how many will I have left over?

___

6. I would like to share £26 between ten people. How much will each person receive and how much will be left?

___

Dear Helper

This activity will help your child to understand that division questions in real life will often involve remainders. Encourage your child to think of a division sentence that will help them and then to try to work out the answers mentally or using jottings. For example, in question 1 your child needs to work out the division sentence 45 divided by 4. Ask: *What in the 4 times-table is near to 45? 44 is 4 x 11 and so 45 divided by 4 = 11 r1. This is not enough time, so we need another month's money. This gives us £48, with £3 as a remainder.* Challenge your child to think of a question with the answer 4 remainder 4.

Name Date

Certain about statements

1. Paul said, 'When I divide by 3, the only remainders I can get are 1 and 2.'

- Investigate this to see if it is true.
- Complete this sentence. Circle true or false.
- I think the statement is true/false because ______________________

____

2. Sally said, 'When I divide by 4, the only remainders I can get are 1, 2 and 3.'

- Investigate this to see if it is true.
- Complete this sentence. Circle true or false.
- I think the statement is true/false because ______________________

____

3. What if you divide a number by 5? What remainders can you get?

- Investigate this to see if it is true.
- Complete this statement:
- I think that if you divide by 5 you can get remainders of ______________________

____

4. What if you divide a number by 10?

- Investigate this to find the possible remainders.
- Complete this statement:
- I think that if you divide by 10 you can get remainders of

____

____

Dear Helper

This activity will help your child to see how remainders work. Encourage your child to start with 10 and divide by 3, then 11 divided by 3, 12 divided by 3 and so on, to see which remainders they can find. Then encourage your child to start with 12 and divide by 4, then 13 divided by 4, 14 divided by 4... to see which remainders they can find. When investigating dividing by 5, start with 10 and work up; when investigating dividing by 10, start with 20 and work up.

Name Date

Talk time

- Ask an adult to show you a recent telephone bill.
- Work out the answers to the following questions.

1. What are the dates covered by the phone bill?
(Hint: it is usually for one or three months) ____________________

to ____________________

2. What is the total cost of the telephone bill?
Round this amount to the nearest £1.00. ____________________

3. How many minutes did your household spend on the phone during this time? ____________________

Round this amount to the nearest 10 minutes ____________________

4. Now work out an approximation of the cost of a call per minute.
Divide the total cost by the number of minutes.

Show how you worked this out here. Ignore any remainders.

Dear Helper
This activity should help your child to see that the skills they are learning at school about problem solving will be useful in life. At school they will be looking at the calculations involved and will be comparing the cost of calls per minute. If you feel uncomfortable about your bill being used in this way, please 'doctor' the bill or prepare a 'pretend' bill. It would be helpful for you to talk through the bill with your child so that they understand that bills come every quarter and that there are charges such as line rental as well as the cost of calls. For extra support, highlight or underline information as you talk it through. As an extra challenge ask: *If this is a typical phone bill, how much would I pay in a whole year?*

Name Date

Close enough?

- Look at the following calculations and decide which is the best approximation.
- Discuss your ideas with an adult

1. Which of these do you think is the best approximation for 609 + 296?

600 + 97
600 + 300
700 + 300
700 + 200
610 + 290

____

2. Which of these do you think is the best approximation for 19 x 7?

20 x 7
2 x 10 x 7
19 x 10
20 x 5

____

3. Which of these do you think is the best approximation for 99 – 67?

100 – 70
100 – 60
100 – 67
99 – 70
99 – 60

____

4. Which of these do you think is the best approximation for 349 – 99?

350 – 90
350 – 100

____

5. Which of these do you think is the best approximation for 999 + 9?

990 + 10
990 + 9
1000 + 9
1000 + 10

____

6. Which of these do you think is the best approximation for 49 x 5?

4 x 10 x 5
5 x 10 x 5

____

Dear Helper

Approximating answers will help your child to know if an answer is correct or sensible without having to rely on a calculator. At school they have learned to round up or down to the nearest 10, so for example, 34 would be rounded down to 30, whereas 35 or 36 would be rounded up to 40. It would help to talk through the various options given before your child makes a decision, as there is sometimes more than one correct answer. As an extension you could challenge your child to work out the exact answers to these questions, which would allow you to compare the estimates with the answer.

Name Date

Focus on fractions

- Look at home to see how many examples of fractions you can find.
- Look in the food cupboard or in the newspaper and ask an adult for some ideas.
- Write, draw or cut out and stick your examples here.
  - ASK PERMISSION before cutting up any newspaper or magazine!

Dear Helper

This week your child is looking at fractions. The aim of this activity is to recognise simple fractions that are several parts of a whole so, while your child is looking for examples, it would be useful if you could emphasise the fact that the fractions are not whole things but parts of a whole object or thing. For example, you might cut a pizza into six pieces (sixths) to share. As a challenge you could ask your child to sort the fractions into those bigger than a half and those smaller than a half.

Equivalence snap

- Cut out and play Snap with these equivalent fraction cards.
- You will need the Snap cards and a helper to play with.

Rules

1. Shuffle the cards and deal them equally between the two players.
2. **Player 1** starts by laying a card on the table.
3. **Player 2** then lays a card next to the first card.
4. Players continue to lay cards on their own piles until two of the cards are equivalent fractions.
5. If a player spots an equivalent fraction they must shout 'Snap!' The other player then has to pick up all the cards that are on the table.
6. The winner is the person to get rid of all of their cards.

- Repeat the game, this time a little faster.

$\frac{1}{2}$	$\frac{2}{4}$	$\frac{8}{16}$
$\frac{4}{8}$	$\frac{1}{4}$	$\frac{2}{8}$
$\frac{1}{5}$	$\frac{2}{10}$	$\frac{1}{8}$
$\frac{2}{16}$	$\frac{1}{10}$	$\frac{2}{20}$

Dear Helper

Equivalent fractions are fractions such as $\frac{1}{2}$ and $\frac{1}{4}$, where the top and bottom numbers of the smaller fraction have both been multiplied by the same number to make the larger fraction. For example: $\frac{1}{4} \times 2 = \frac{2}{8}$. If your child fails to spot an equivalent fraction, ask them, for example: *What is double 1? What is double 4?* It would also help to move your finger between the two top numbers (numerators) and then between the two bottom numbers (denominators), so that they can spot the connection.

Name Date

Favourite days

■ Look at the bar chart and answer the following questions.

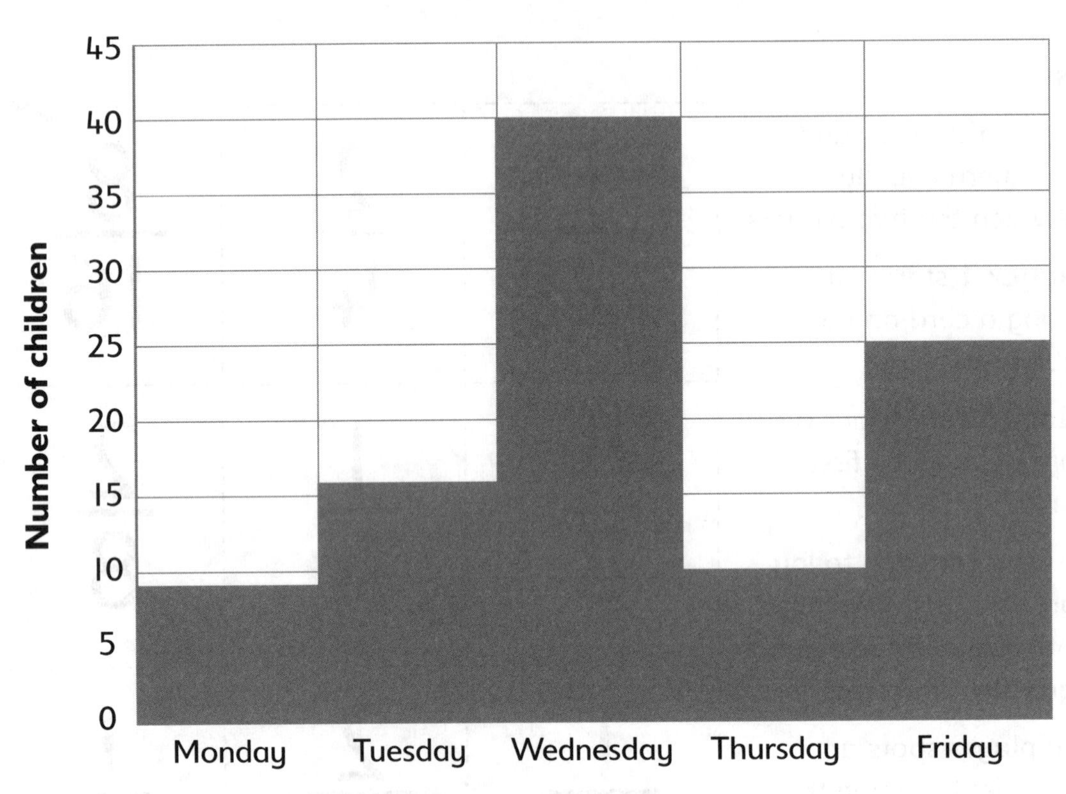

1. How many children took part in the survey?
2. What was the favourite day of the week?
3. On what day of the week did ten children vote?
4. What is the difference between the number of votes on Thursday and the number of votes on Wednesday?
5. Why do you think Wednesday could be a popular day of the week?
6. If 16 children voted Tuesday as their favourite day of the week, how many children voted Monday as their favourite day?

Dear Helper

This graph is called a bar chart, on which the intervals have been labelled in 5s. Your child will find it easy to read off the intervals of 5 and 10 (Wednesday and Friday), but will find it more difficult to read Monday and Tuesday. Encourage your child to make an estimate and remind them that 100 children took part in the survey. As an extra challenge ask your child to redraw this bar chart using intervals of 2, or try to draw a bar chart on a computer if one is available.

Activity name	Learning objectives	Content of homework	Managing the homework	All New 100 Maths Lessons Year 4	
				NNS	Page
Rounding off	• **Round any positive integer less than 1000 to the nearest 10 or 100.**	**Maths to share** Children play a game with an adult. The success of the game relies on the children deciding if their cards can be rounded up or down to match the 'key card'.	**Before:** Demonstrate the game. **After:** Ask for examples of other numbers that can be rounded to the nearest 10 or 100.	1	152
Beat the clock	• Use known number facts and place value to add or subtract mentally, including any pair of two-digit whole numbers.	**Homework activity** Addition and subtraction questions to be read out by a helper and answered mentally or with rough jottings.	**Before:** Discuss methods that children can use to help them answer the questions. **After:** Choose a few children to tell you how long it took them to answer the questions and which they found the most difficult.	2	155
Column skills	• **Develop written methods for column addition of whole numbers less than 1000.**	**Maths homework** Children are asked to set out and work out some column additions and then to check their answers using another written method or talking through a mental method.	**Before:** Discuss how to set out and work out addition totals. Recap checking techniques. **After:** Go through individual examples.	2	156
Subtracting columns	• **Develop and refine written methods for column subtraction of two whole numbers less than 1000.**	**Maths homework** Children are asked to set out and work out some column subtractions and then to check their answers using another written method or talking through a mental method.	**Before:** Discuss how to set out and work out subtraction totals. Recap checking techniques. **After:** Go through individual examples.	3	161
Bright white	• Use all four operations to solve word problems involving money using one or more steps, including converting pounds to pence.	**Puzzles to do at home** Children are asked to investigate the cost of three types of toothpaste and a tube of toothpaste from their local shop.	**Before:** Discuss 'finding the difference' and revise how to multiply by 10. **After:** Compare results. Which toothpaste was the best value for money? How much could the family save over a year?	3	165

Teacher's notes

Activity name	Learning objectives	Content of homework	Managing the homework	All New 100 Maths Lessons Year 4	
				NNS	Page
Estimating and measuring capacity	**• Suggest suitable units and measuring equipment to estimate or measure capacity.**	**Maths to share** Children are asked to estimate capacities and collect labels showing capacity from food packets.	**Before:** Discuss which sorts of packets would be suitable to measure and bring in, and how to use a measuring jug at home. **After:** Look at packaging. Ask: *Is the capacity clearly displayed?*	4	170
Parts of a litre	• Begin to recognise the equivalent of one half, one quarter, three quarters and one tenth of 1 litre in millilitres.	**Puzzles to do at home** Children match up corresponding parts of a litre.	**Before:** Recap equivalent measures, for example 500ml = ½ litre = 0.5 litre. **After:** Compare and discuss the answers.	4	170
Nutty nets	• Visualise 3-D shapes from 2-D drawings and identify simple nets of solid shapes.	**Maths to share** Children are asked to look at nets in the home and to make a 3-D shape from a net using squared paper.	**Before:** Talk through the method of making a net of a cube; discuss faces, and the use of flaps. Provide the children with squared paper for making their own nets. **After:** Compare and display 3-D shapes.	5	178
Polyfolds	**• Classify polygons using criteria such as number of right angles, whether or not they are regular, symmetry properties.** • Make shapes: for example, construct polygons by paper folding.	**Puzzles to do at home** Children are challenged to fold squares using a specific number of folds to form different polygons.	**Before:** Revise the names of polygons with various numbers of sides. Clarify the difference between irregular and regular shapes. **After:** Share the different solutions as a class.	5	177
Finding directions	• Make clockwise and anti-clockwise turns. • Recognise positions and directions. • Recognise simple examples of horizontal and vertical lines.	**Maths to share** Children are asked to follow instructions to draw on a piece of A4 paper. The instructions are read out by an adult.	**Before:** Recap horizontal, vertical, clockwise, anti-clockwise, right, left, 180° and 90° turns. **After:** Share the drawings and discuss what was the most difficult part of the task.	6	182

Activity name	Learning objectives	Content of homework	Managing the homework	All New 100 Maths Lessons Year 4	
				NNS	**Page**
Numbers against the clock	• Recognise and extend number sequences formed by counting from any number in steps of constant size, extending beyond zero when counting back.	**Maths to share** A game for two players to practise number sequences.	**Before:** Run through the rules of the game. Play the game, adjusting the timings as necessary. **After:** Ask: *Who won? How far did you get with each sequence?*	**8**	**188**
Multiple magic	• Recognise multiples of 2, 3, 4, 5, and 10, up to tenth multiple.	**Puzzles to do at home** Children are asked to identify numbers from clues given about their multiples.	**Before:** Explain to the children how being logical with their working will help them find the answer, and how writing a list of numbers and then eliminating some may also help. **After:** Ask: *Which were the numbers? Can you explain why?*	**8**	**185**
Dividing codes	• **Derive quickly division facts corresponding to 2, 3, 4, 5 and 10 times-tables**.	**Maths homework** Children are asked to colour-code numbers divisible by 2, 3, 4, 5 and 10.	**Before:** Recap the various methods of checking that numbers are in the 2, 3, 4, 5 and 10 times-tables. Revise that if a number is divisible by, for example, 2 and 3 it is also divisible by 6. **After:** Talk through the answers and methods.	**9**	**193**
Matching sentences	• Understand the principle (not the name) of the distributive law as it applies to multiplication.	**Maths homework** Children are asked to match up various multiplication number sentences that have the same answer.	**Before:** Remind the children that, for example, $2 \times 3 \times 4 = 2 \times 4 \times 3$ or $3 \times 4 \times 2$ and that multiplying by 1 does not change an answer. **After:** Check the answers together, focusing on alternative methods of writing, for example 7×8 ($7 \times 4 \times 2$ or $7 \times 2 \times 2 \times 2$).	**9**	**191**
Number products	• Develop and refine written methods for TU × U.	**Maths homework** Children are asked to find the products of different numbers, using a written method. They are then asked to find the difference between the largest and smallest answers.	**Before:** Recap the various written methods of finding products. Check that the children remember what is meant by 'find the difference'. **After:** Talk through the answers and methods.	**10**	**201**

Teacher's notes

Activity name	Learning objectives	Content of homework	Managing the homework	All New 100 Maths Lessons Year 4	
				NNS	Page
Higher or lower?	• Order simple fractions: for example, decide whether fractions such as $^3/_8$ or $^7/_{10}$ are greater than or less than one half.	**Maths homework** Children are asked to colour code a set of fractions to determine whether they are above or below ½.	**Before:** Order some fractions on a number line marked with 0, ½ and 1. **After:** Review the activity and ask for some other examples of fractions that are greater or less than ½.	11	208
Decimals equal fractions	• Recognise the equivalence between the decimal and fraction forms.	**Maths homework** Children are asked to colour in sets of equivalent fractions.	**Before:** Talk through the colour coding and revise equivalence. **After:** Check equivalent fraction groups.	11	210
Trans-Air challenge	• Estimate/check times using seconds, minutes, hours. • Read simple timetables.	**Maths homework** Children are asked to plan a journey using an airline timetable.	**Before:** Review and discuss how to work out time durations from the timetable. **After:** Look at the timetable. Ask: *How many hours does the Trans-Air plane spend in the air each week?*	12	214
Money columns	• **Develop and refine written methods for column addition and subtraction of two whole numbers less than 1000.**	**Maths homework** Activity designed to consolidate children's understanding of column addition involving decimals or money.	**Before:** Recap on how to set out addition calculations involving money using squared paper. If appropriate, set a limit on the number of calculations and combinations to be found. **After:** Compare answers and check that the children were able to find an appropriate number of calculations.	12	215
Carroll families	• Solve a problem by collecting, classifying, organising, representing and interpreting data in Carroll diagrams.	**Puzzles to do at home** Children are asked to investigate the statement 'Most people over the age of 15 own a mobile telephone' using a Carroll diagram to represent the collected data.	**Before:** Remind the children how to fill in a Carroll diagram. **After:** Discuss the findings and the statement.	13	221
Workout pictograms	• Solve a problem by collecting, classifying, organising, representing and interpreting data in pictograms (symbols representing 2, 5, 10 or 20 units).	**Maths homework** Children are asked to complete a pictogram and then redraw it to a different scale, using pencil and paper or a computer representation. The aim is to present the data as clearly as possible.	**Before:** Stress to the children that the aim is to make their work as clear as possible. Discuss the layout of the pictogram and the use of keys and labels. **After:** Compare representations.	13	222

Rounding numbers

- This is a game for two or more players.
  - Write these numbers (right) on separate pieces of card or paper:
  - Cut out the 'Round to...' key cards and three-digit number cards.
  - Deal out the three-digit number cards face down, equally between the players.
  - Lay one larger key card face up in the middle.
  - **Player 1** should then turn over his/her top number card and round it as instructed on the key card.
  - If Player 1 is correct the card is discarded and he or she has another go. If not, Player 1 must keep the card and place it at the bottom of their pile. **Player 2** then takes a turn.
  - Continue until all the cards have been correctly rounded according to the first key card, then turn over a new key card and continue.
  - The winner is the player to get rid of all their cards.
- Repeat with the key cards in a different order and increase the speed of play.

	421	422	423
445	446	447	448
449	461	462	463
464	465	466	467
468	469		

Round to the nearest 100

Round to the nearest 10

Dear Helper

This activity will reinforce the idea of rounding to the nearest 10 or 100. If a number ends in 0, 1, 2, 3 or 4 it is rounded down, so 463 would be 460 to the nearest 10, whereas numbers ending in 5, 6, 7, 8 or 9 are rounded up, so 467 would be 470 rounded to the nearest 10. In a similar way, when rounding to the nearest 100, numbers up to 449 are rounded down to 400, and numbers 450 and above are rounded up to 500. When your child chooses a card, ask them to discuss their reasoning with you, for example, *464 ends in a 4, so rounded to the nearest 10 it will be 460.* As an extra challenge ask: *What other numbers could be rounded according to your key card?*

Name Date

Beat the clock

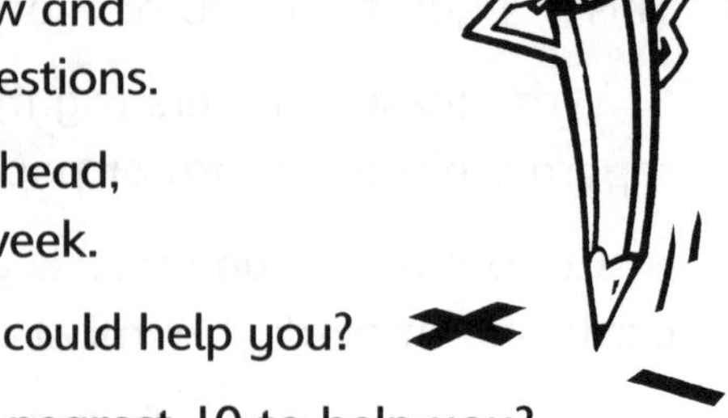

- Ask your helper to read out the questions below and time how long it takes you to answer all 20 questions.
- Work out the answers to the questions in your head, using the methods that you have learned this week.

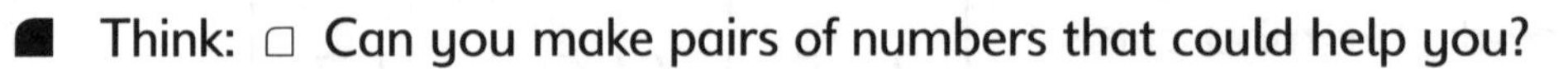

- Think: ☐ Can you make pairs of numbers that could help you?

  ☐ Can you round the number up to the nearest 10 to help you?

23 – 19 = ☐	23 – 21 = ☐	36 – 28 = ☐
87 – 19 = ☐	45 + 21 = ☐	70 – 38 = ☐
45 + 19 = ☐	26 – 21 = ☐	37 + 28 = ☐
26 – 19 = ☐	36 – 21 = ☐	56 – 8 = ☐
36 – 29 = ☐	70 – 31 = ☐	25 + 57 = ☐
37 + 29 = ☐	87 – 28 = ☐	29 + 13 = ☐
27 + 9 = ☐	46 + 18 = ☐	

- How many did you get right?
  - ☐ How long did it take you?
- Look at the questions again to see if you could have made things easier for yourself by using the methods you have been learning in class. Now repeat the test.
  - ☐ How many did you get right?
  - ☐ How long did it take you?

Dear Helper

This activity will help your child to develop methods for adding and subtracting mentally. If your child is stuck, say, for example: *For 37 + 29, you can work out 37 + 30 and then take away 1.* For subtraction it may help to subtract the nearest multiple of 10 then add on the difference. For example, say: *For 36 – 28, work out 36 – 30. You have subtracted 2 too many so add that on at the end.* At the end of the timed activity go through the questions with your child and ask: *How did you work that one out?* As a challenge your child could try to think of another mental method to use to answer the questions.

Name Date

Column skills

- Look at the pairs of numbers below.
- Using the space provided, set out and work out the total of the two numbers using the column method that you have been learning at school this week.
  - An example has been included (right) to help you.

	1	4	5
+		8	9
	2	3	4
	1	1	

(check: 145 + 90 = 235, then subtract 1, so the total is 234)

			4	5	5						2	3	3						1	6	9		
		+		3	9					+		1	8					+		1	9		

			5	7	7						6	8	9						8	9	4		
		+		9	9					+		2	7					+		2	8		

Dear Helper

This exercise will help reinforce the skills that your child has been learning this week at school about adding in columns. Please encourage your child to set out the questions carefully, ensuring that the units are beneath the units, tens beneath the tens and the hundreds beneath the hundreds. Ask your child to talk you through each stage of the calculation, especially any 'carrying' over to the next column. When your child is happy with their answer, encourage them to find an alternative method to check their answer, either by jotting something different down at the side or mentally by talking it through.

Name Date

Subtracting columns

- Look at the pairs of numbers below.
- Using the space provided, set out and work out the answers to the subtraction questions below using the column method that you have been learning at school this week.

145 − 89	233 − 14	168 − 14
577 − 98	684 − 27	894 − 28

Dear Helper
This exercise will help reinforce the skills that your child has been learning this week at school about subtracting in columns. Please encourage your child to set out the questions carefully, ensuring that the units are beneath the units, tens beneath the tens and the hundreds beneath the hundreds. Ask your child to talk you through each stage of the calculation, especially any 'carrying' over to the next column. When your child is happy with their answer, encourage them to find an alternative method to check their answer, either by jotting something down at the side or mentally by talking it through.

Name Date

Bright white

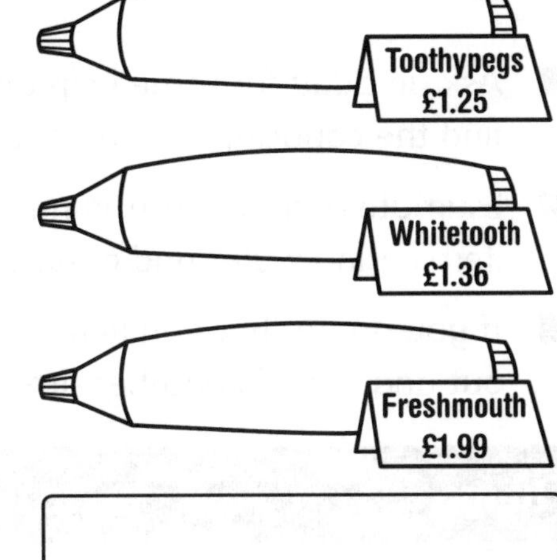

- Look in your local supermarket or shop to find out the price of another tube of toothpaste.
- Draw a picture of the toothpaste tube in the box provided and add the price to the tag.
- Investigate the differences in the prices of the different tubes of toothpaste. Write your results below.

____

____

____

- Imagine that a family of four uses ten tubes of toothpaste in a year.
- How much could they save in a year by using the cheapest toothpaste rather than the most expensive?
- Write your results and workings below.

Dear Helper

This activity covers word problems involving numbers and money in real-life situations. Encourage your child to record their results logically, comparing two toothpastes before looking at another pair and to write down everything that they observe or find out. If visiting the shop or supermarket, observe the differences in price of 'branded' toothpastes and the shop's own brand. A more complex challenge would involve comparing different sizes of tubes or packaging, the quantity of toothpaste and prices, for example: *Is toothpaste cheaper in tubes or in pump dispensers?*

Name Date

Estimating and measuring capacity

- Ask an adult for some help and permission to find the capacity of some household items.
- Estimate and measure, in millilitres, the following items using water and a measuring jug.
- If you do not have an item on the list, cross it out and write in another similar item.

Item	Estimate in millilitres	Capacity in millilitres
A cup		
A mug		
A small bowl		
A small saucepan		
An empty carton or can		

- Now look in your food cupboard or fridge to see if there are any packets or bottles with the capacity written on them.
- Look for a bottle or can that holds between 100 millilitres and 500 millilitres.
- Write the details below or take an empty packet/bottle/can to school to show your teacher.

____

____

Dear Helper

This activity will help your child to understand the relationship between different capacities. They have been learning about millilitres and litres at school this week. Estimating is a difficult but important life skill. It may help your child if they find the capacity of one object and then use that as a guide for other objects. Ask: *Will this hold more or less?* As an extra challenge you could estimate, with your child, the capacity of larger items such as a kitchen sink.

Name Date

Parts of a litre

- You will need some coloured pencils for this activity.
- Look at the cans and bottles below and see if you can colour those with the same capacities in the same colour.

- Now look in your store cupboard or fridge at home.
- Can you find any packaging with the same capacity?

Dear Helper
This activity should help reinforce the equivalent ways of writing capacities, using fractions and decimals. Encourage your child to think of the largest capacities and find the matching pair (or three) and then the smallest. If possible, match up some of the capacities with packaging of cartons or cans from home so that the child starts to visualise the 'size' of each capacity. Making different piles of the equivalent measures as you find them will help with this. As an extra challenge ask: *Which ways can you write 10.5 litres? ... 20¼ litres? ... 100.75 litres?*

Name Date

Nutty nets

- Nets are the flat pattern for a 3-D shape, for example if you took a cereal packet from the cupboard and opened it flat, this would give you the net of a cuboid.

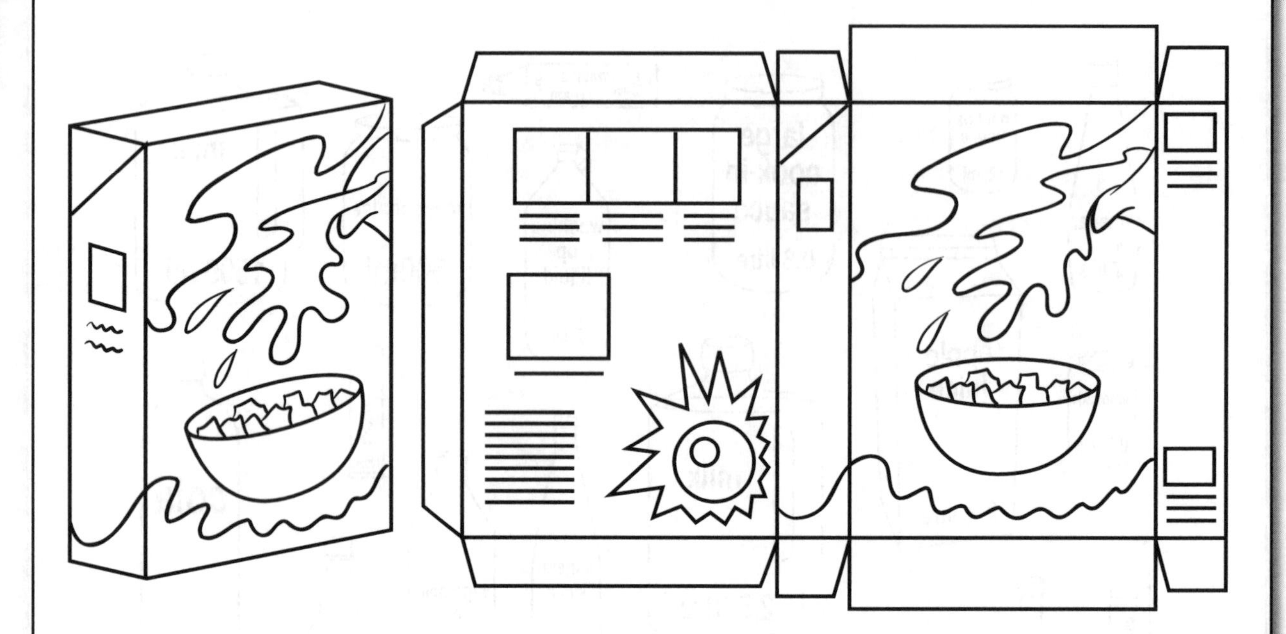

- You will need some squared paper.
- Look around your house for an empty packet.
  - ☐ Ask permission to cut it open, lay it flat and look at the net.
  - ☐ Take a few minutes to refold it back into a 3-D shape and then dismantle again to look at the net.
  - ☐ Carefully draw the net of a 3-D shape on the sheet of squared paper.
  - ☐ Look at the faces and remember that the net may need flaps if you want to glue the 3-D shape together.
  - ☐ When you are sure, cut out your net and see if it folds into a 3-D shape.
  - ☐ Decorate your 3-D shape if you have time.

Dear Helper
In school your child will have looked at various nets of a cube and how they fold to make the cube. Your child might have trouble visualising how the shape will fold up, so encourage them to look at the opposite faces and how the shape will look from the top, bottom, the sides, etc. As an extra challenge, ask your child to sketch a different net that will fold to make the same shape.

Name Date

Polyfolds

- Cut out this square to help you with these puzzles.
- By folding your square in different ways, see if you can create these different polygons.
  - ☐ One fold to create an isosceles triangle.
  - ☐ One fold to create an irregular pentagon.
  - ☐ Two folds to create an irregular pentagon.
  - ☐ Two folds to form an irregular hexagon.
  - ☐ One fold to create another quadrilateral.
  - ☐ Two folds to create an isosceles triangle.
  - ☐ Three folds to create an irregular heptagon.
  - ☐ Four folds to create a regular hexagon.
- If you find a way of creating the polygon, mark the fold on the squares on the right with a dotted line so that you can discuss your findings with your teacher and the rest of the class.
- What other polygons can you make by folding a square?
  - ☐ Show any other results on the squares on the left.

Dear Helper

This activity reinforces the shape work that your child has been revising this week. Encourage your child to cut out and use the large square to help them investigate folding to create other polygons. An isosceles triangle has two sides of the same length and one of a different length; a pentagon has five sides; a hexagon has six sides; a quadrilateral has four sides; a heptagon has seven sides. A regular shape has all sides the same length and an irregular shape has sides of different lengths. As an extra challenge, encourage your child to write instructions similar to those given above to direct others to make the extra shapes that they have recorded.

Name Date

Following directions

- To do this activity you must be sitting down with a pencil and a blank piece of A4 paper in front of you.
- Ask an adult to make sure that your piece of paper is portrait way up in front of you.
- Then, ask them to read out the following instructions, ONCE ONLY.
  - ☐ Turn your paper around 90 degrees.
  - ☐ Draw a horizontal line across the middle of the page, so that your page is divided in half.
  - ☐ In the top right-hand corner of the page draw a circle.
  - ☐ Draw a vertical line from the circle to the middle of the page.
  - ☐ Write your name in the bottom right-hand corner of the page.
  - ☐ Turn your page around 90 degrees so that the circle is at the bottom of the page.
  - ☐ Draw a square on the right-hand side of the page.
  - ☐ Turn the page 180 degrees.
  - ☐ Draw a horizontal line from one corner of the square to the line in the middle of the page.
  - ☐ Now turn your sheet 90 degrees clockwise.
  - ☐ Now put your pencil down.
- Ask the adult to re-read the instructions, going through each step carefully.
- How good were you at following instructions?
- Take your picture to school and compare it with your friends.

Dear Helper
This activity encourages your child to listen to and follow instructions. Make sure that you do not repeat any of the instructions until your child has put their pen down. Before your child starts, it may help to revise the words horizontal (across the page), vertical (up/down the page), 90° (¼ of a turn), 180° (½ a turn), clockwise/anti-clockwise, left and right. As an extra challenge you could include some extra instructions such as: *Draw a triangle in the bottom left-hand corner* or *Draw a star in the square*. For checking purposes, note down any extra instructions that you give.

Numbers against the clock

- You will need:
  - ☐ scissors (to cut out the cards)
  - ☐ a stopwatch or clock
  - ☐ a partner to play the game with.

Rule: add 2	Rule: add 3	Rule: subtract 3	Rule: add 10	Rule: add 9	Rule: take away 5
Rule: add 11	Rule: add 4	Rule: add 6	Rule: take away 7	Rule: minus 8	Rule: minus 4

- Instructions
  - ☐ Prepare the following numbers on separate pieces of card or paper, to be starting numbers:

    1 5 7 9 19 33 38 39 57 99 100
  - ☐ Cut out the cards above and shuffle both sets so that you have two piles of cards, one with rules and one with starting numbers.
  - ☐ **Player 1** picks one card from each pile and places them face up.
  - ☐ Player 1 then has one minute to call out as many numbers as he/she can in the sequence.
  - ☐ **Player 2** records how many correct numbers in the sequence are called out. Play continues either for one minute or until an incorrect number is called out.
  - ☐ Play then moves to Player 2.
  - ☐ Play continues until all the cards are used.
- The winner is the player who says the most correct numbers.

Dear Helper
This game will help your child practise number sequences, such as 'add 2'. If your child is finding it difficult to call out the numbers in a sequence, allow them to write the sequence on a piece of paper. As an added challenge, choose larger starting numbers, for example 120, 134, 178 or 199.

Name Date

Multiple magic

■ Find the numbers from the clues below about their multiples.

I am an even number and a multiple of 3. I am less than 10. Who am I? ________	I am an odd multiple of 5. I am less than 20 but greater than 10. Who am I? ________
I am less than 100 but greater than 80. I am a multiple of 10. Who am I? ________	I am a multiple of 4 and 5. I am greater than 40 but less than 80. Who am I? ________
I am an even number. I am a multiple of 3 and 4. I am less than 50. Which numbers could I be? ________	I am an even number. I am greater than 50 but less than 80. I am a multiple of 4. Which numbers could I be? ________
I am a multiple of 2, 3, 4 and 5. What is the smallest number that I could be? ________	I am a multiple of 3 and 5. What is the smallest number that I could be? ________
I am a multiple of 2 and 5. What is the largest two-digit number that I could be? ________	

Dear Helper

This activity aims to reinforce the work that your child has been doing in school about multiples. A multiple is a number larger than the original number in its times-table. So, for example, multiples of 5 are 10, 15, 20, 25, 30 and so on; multiples of 3 are 6, 9, 12, 15, 18 and so on. Encourage your child to write down a list of numbers and then to eliminate them slowly as they work through the clue. For example, for the clue, *I am an even number and a multiple of 3. I am less than 10. Who am I?* Encourage your child to write down a list of even numbers that are less than 10 (2, 4, 6, 8) and then to think about which number is in the 3 times-table (6).

Name Date

Dividing codes

- You will need some coloured pens or pencils for this activity.
- Follow the instructions below.
  - Circle in yellow the numbers that are divisible by 2 and 3.
  - Put a blue box around the numbers that are divisible by 2 and 5.
  - Put a green triangle around the numbers that are divisible 3 and 4.
  - Put a red rectangle around the numbers that are divisible by 4 and 5.
  - Some numbers may have more than one code.

6	12	18	20	36
72	40	45	70	78
60	80	160	30	100
34	56	24	88	90

- Challenge: Can you think of a number that would be coloured yellow, blue, green and red? Write it below, showing any workings.

Dear Helper
This activity challenges your child to follow instructions and to think about numbers that are in the 2, 3, 4, 5 and 10 times-tables. If your child is finding it difficult to work out, for example, the numbers that are in the 2 times-table and then 3 times-table, remind them that if a number is in the 2 and 3 times table it will also be in the 6 times-table. As an extra challenge ask your child to think of *any* numbers that would be coloured red and green.

Name Date

Matching sentences

- Match up the number sentences that have the same answer by drawing a line between them.

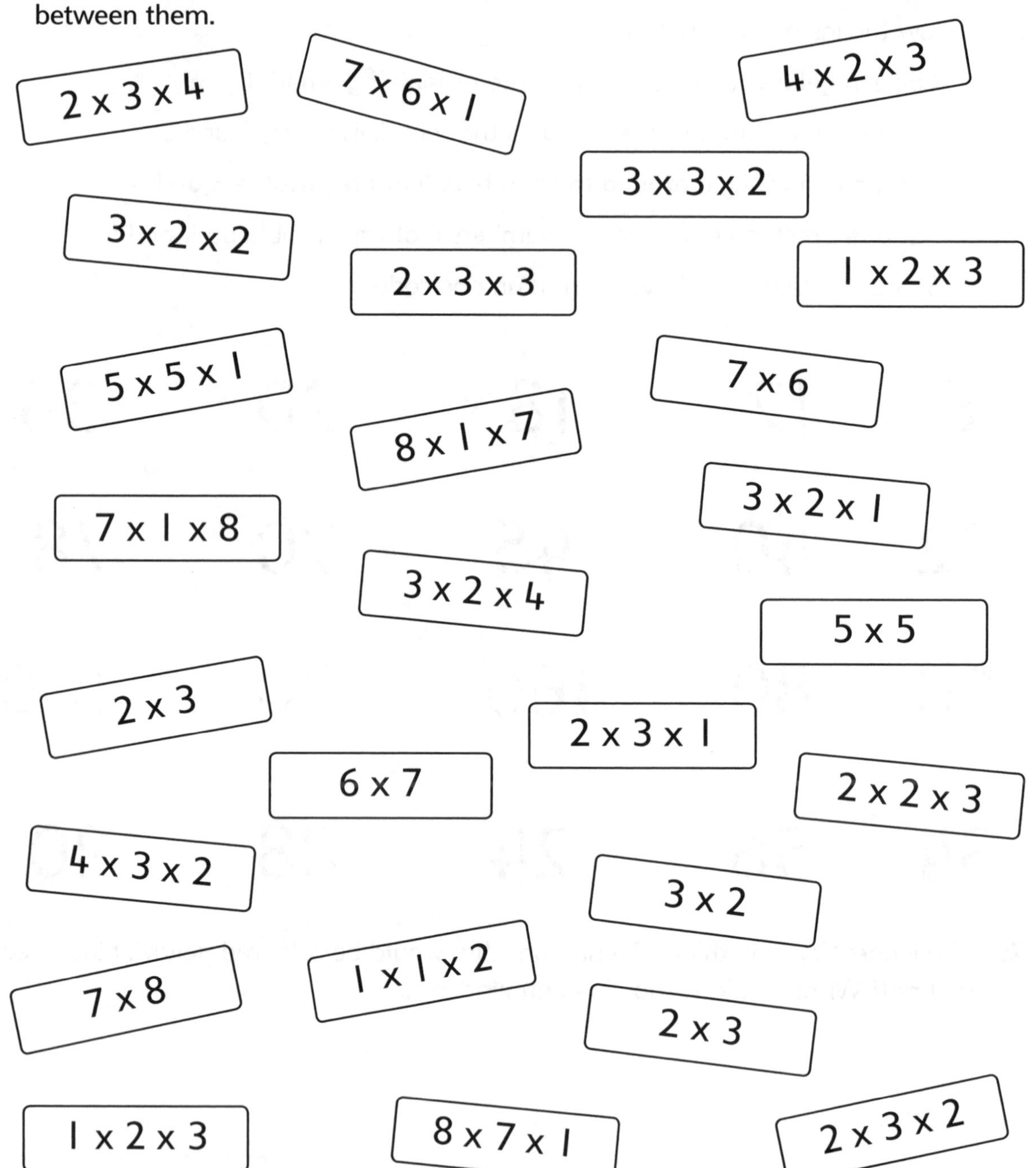

Dear Helper

This activity aims to reinforce the idea that multiplication sentences give the same answer regardless of the order in which the numbers are written. For example, $6 \times 7 = 7 \times 6$. Also, if a number is multiplied by 1, the number remains the same. If your child is finding this difficult to grasp, allow them to work out a few of the calculations on a piece of paper. For an extra challenge ask, for example: *How else can you write* 7×6*?* ($7 \times 2 \times 3$) or 7×8*?* ($7 \times 4 \times 2$).

Name Date

Number products

2	3	4	5	6	7	8	9
12	23	34	45	56	67	78	89

- See what products you can make by multiplying one of the single-digit numbers above by one of the two-digit numbers.
- Record your written workings in the space below.

- Challenge: See if you can find the largest possible product and then the smallest possible product.

Dear Helper
This activity aims to revise the skills that your child has been learning this week about using written methods to help solve multiplication questions. Your child has been taught a variety of ways to work out questions and can use any that they would like. Examples of how to work out 24 x 6 are as follows:

a)

x	20	4
6	120	24

= 144

b)
```
  24
x  6
  24 (6 x 4)
 120 (6 x 20)
 144 (6 x 24)
```

c)
```
  24
x  6
 144
  2
```

Name Date

Higher or lower?

- You will need some coloured pencils or pens.
- Colour these fractions according to the instructions below:

Less than $\frac{1}{2}$ colour in red.

More than $\frac{1}{2}$ colour in yellow.

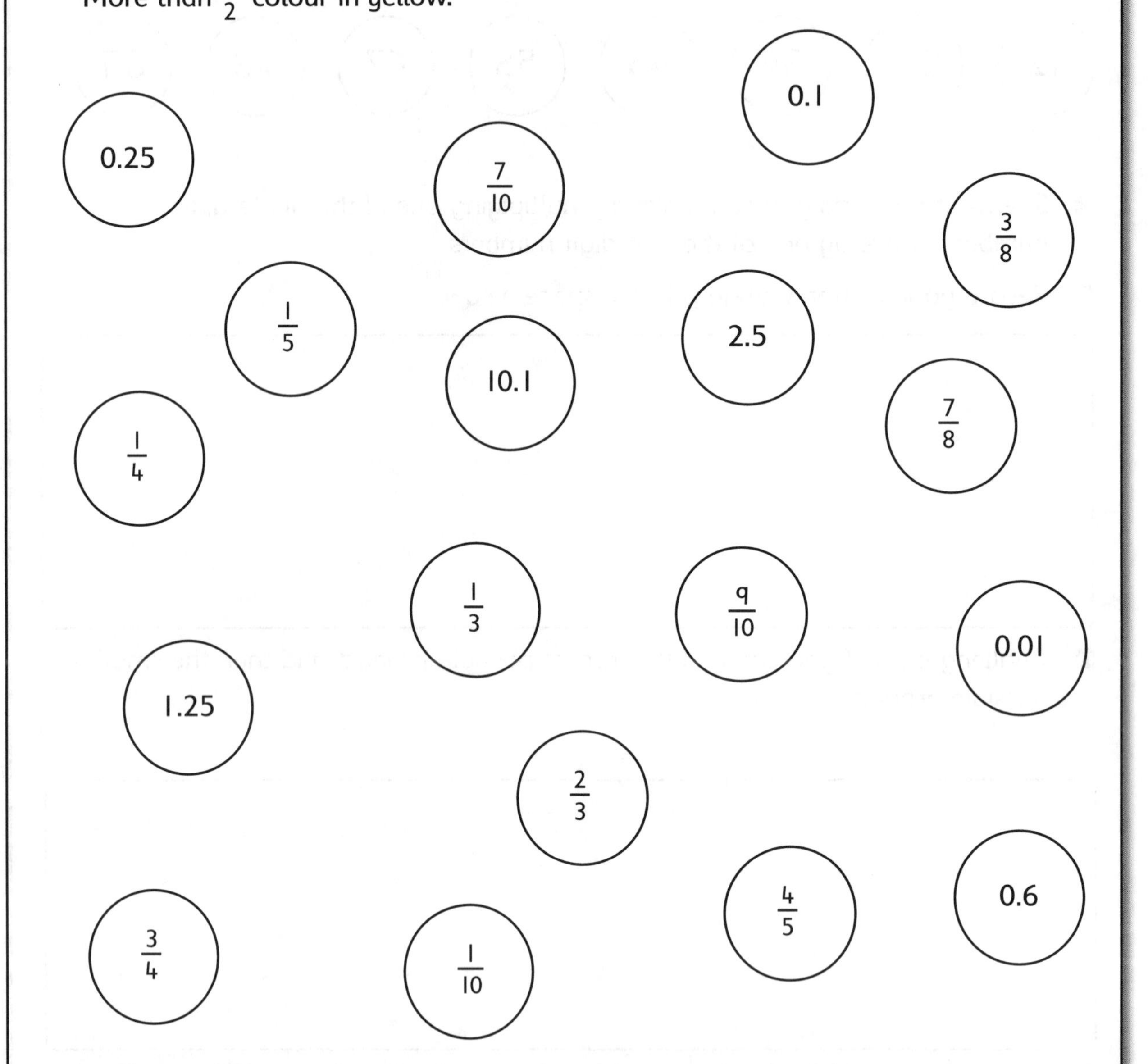

Dear Helper

This activity will help your child to order fractions and decimals. Encourage your child to think about equivalent fractions if they are unsure. Equivalent fractions, such as $\frac{1}{2}$ and $\frac{4}{8}$ are fractions where the top number and the bottom number of the first fraction have both been multiplied by the same number to make the second fraction. For example: $\frac{1}{4} = \frac{2}{8}$ where $\frac{1}{4}$ multiplied by 2 top and bottom is $\frac{2}{8}$. Because $\frac{1}{4} = \frac{2}{8}$ and $\frac{1}{2} = \frac{4}{8}$, $\frac{1}{4}$ is less than $\frac{1}{2}$. As an extra challenge, ask your child to add other fractions or decimals to the list and colour code them as greater than or less than $\frac{1}{2}$.

Name Date

Decimals equal fractions

- Look at the containers below.
  - ☐ See if you can spot two containers with equal capacities or masses.
  - ☐ When you spot matching containers, colour them in the same colour.
  - ☐ Beware! Some of the containers do not have a match. Leave these uncoloured.

Dear Helper

This activity aims to help your child make the link between decimals and fractions, eg $\frac{1}{2}$ = 0.5. First, encourage them to focus on the measurements, for example pints, then focus on the numbers to see if the amounts are the same. As an extra challenge ask: *What would measure approximately $2\frac{1}{4}$ grams? ...1.4 pints? ... $3\frac{1}{3}$ oz?*

Name Date

Trans-Air challenge

- Look at the Trans-Air schedule below.
  - It shows their winter flights from London Gatwick to Nice.
  - The planes fly from London Gatwick to Nice, and then turn around and come back again.

Day	Monday	Wednesday	Thursday	Friday	Sunday
Flight No.	PJ203	PJ204	PJ205	PJ206	PJ207
Depart Gatwick	10.05	10.15	10.05	10.00	9.55
Arrive Nice	11.40	11.50	11.40	11.35	11.30
Depart Nice	12.15	12.25	12.10	12.10	12.05
Arrive Gatwick	13.55	14.05	13.55	13.50	13.45

1. How long is the flight from Gatwick to Nice? __________
2. Does it take the same amount of time each day? __________
3. Does it take the same amount of time to fly back to London each day? __________
4. On which day of the week does it take longer? __________
5. How much longer? __________
6. If I was planning to travel to Nice for the weekend, leaving London on Friday and returning on Sunday, how much time would I spend in the air? __________
7. If my plane on Sunday was delayed leaving Nice by 25 minutes, at what time would I land at Gatwick? __________

Dear Helper

This activity will help your child learn how to plan journeys and use timetables in 'real-life' situations. It may be useful to use a ruler or a piece of paper to help your child to read each line of a timetable. As an extra challenge, ask your child to work out how long the Trans-Air plane is in the air each week.

Name Date

Money columns

- Find the sums of all of the pairs of the following numbers (for example, £13.56 + £8.76, £13.56 + £6.78 and so on – there will be 15 sums in total): £13.56 £8.76 £6.78 £3.14 £2.99 £8.12
- Set out your work using the squared paper below and be sure to keep your decimal points underneath each other, for example:

```
   £ 8 . 7 6
 + £ 6 . 7 8
  £1 5 . 5 4
     1   1
```

Dear Helper

This activity aims to reinforce the work that your child has been doing in class about adding amounts of money in columns. The most important aspect of this is to set out the sum carefully so that the pounds are written beneath the pounds, the pence beneath the pence and the decimal points are directly below each other. Encourage your child to check their calculation with a mental strategy to see if their answer is appropriate, before going on to the next pair. If time allows, challenge your child to find the difference between pairs of numbers. Stress that again the decimal points must line up beneath each other and that the largest amount of money must go on the top (take away the smaller amount from the larger amount).

Name Date

Carroll families

- Write the names of ten people from your family, friends or neighbours in the correct positions on the Carroll diagram below.

	Owns a mobile phone	Does not own a mobile phone
15 years old or younger		
Not 15 years old or younger		

- Use this information to help you decide if the following statement is true or false:

  Most people in the UK over 15 years of age own a mobile telephone.

  True/False

- Take your completed sheet into school so that you can discuss your findings with the rest of your class.

Dear Helper
This activity aims to show your child that a Carroll diagram can be used to organise information. If you cannot find ten people locally to survey, perhaps your child could think of friends or members of their family who they know fit into one of the boxes. As an extra challenge ask: *How else could you sort this information?*

Name Date

Workout pictograms

☺ = 5 children

Hours	Number of children
Less than 1 hour	☺☺
Less than 2 hours	☺☺☺☺
Less than 3 hours	☺☺☺☺☺☺☺
Less than 4 hours	☺☺☺
4 hours or more	

- This pictogram shows the number of hours of exercise 100 children took in one week.
- Fill in the 'More than 4 hours' row. Remember that all the rows must add up to 100 in total.
- Now, using the data in the pictogram above, draw another pictogram below to represent the same data using the scale ☺ = 10 children.
  - Remember that you may have to use half a ☺ to represent 5 children.
  - The main aim is to make your results very clear for the reader. You may use a computer if you like.
- At school you will be comparing your presentation with the others in your class.

☺ = 10 children

Hours	Number of children
Less than 1 hour	
Less than 2 hours	
Less than 3 hours	
Less than 4 hours	
4 hours or more	

Dear Helper

This activity reinforces work that your child has been doing on handling data. Your child has been taught how to draw pictograms and bar charts, and how to use a computer to present data. Encourage them to take plenty of time, use a large enough scale and to use most of the space on the page to make their pictograms as clear as possible to the reader.

Answer sheet

Autumn term

P15 Money, money, money!

1 20 weeks. **2** £7.20. **3** £2.03. **4** 4 bars.

P16 Adding

1 100 + 10 = 110. **2** 160 + 12 = 172. **3** 100 + 60 + 8 = 168. **4** 200 + 110 + 14 = 324.

P19 Converting lengths

2cm	450mm
0.1m	6000m
300cm	800cm
0.2km	40cm
700mm	3.5m

P21 The shortest distance

120cm, 8m, 2m, 500cm,
420cm, 345cm,
320cm.

P22 Find the treasure

(3,3)

P24 Sums and products

(8, 6); (9, 7); (5, 5); (8, 3); (7, 6); (9, 4).

P25 Multiplication and division practice

392	415
7	12

P27 Missing signs

+; –; ×; –; ÷.

P28 Fraction shapes

$^{2}/_{4}$ or ½
$^{1}/_{3}$
$^{2}/_{6}$ or $^{1}/_{3}$
½ or $^{3}/_{6}$
$^{2}/_{10}$ or $^{1}/_{5}$

P30 Counting on

1 388. **2** 544. **3** 268. **4** 915. **5** 359. **6** 766.

P33 Times-tables practice

The two numbers that do not fit in the tables are 19 and 23.

Spring term

P39 Timed challenge

1 40
2 68
3 40
4 12
5 29
6 90
7 66
8 60
9 21
10 21

P40 The crossing-out challenge

9
1 and 99
76 and 75
33 and 43, 63 and 73, 12 and 22
14
19
50 and 52
27

P45 Colour by numbers

6 red	7 blue	8 green	9 yellow	10
16 green	17	45 yellow	19	20
26	27 yellow	28 blue	29	30 red
35 blue	37	38	39	40 green
14 blue	21 blue	12 red	49 blue	50
2	57	58	59	60 red
66 red	32 green	64 green	69	70 blue

1 6 + 30 + 12 + 60 + 66 = 174.
2 64 – 8 = 56. **3** 4.

P47 Angle grinding

4	1	7	5
3	8	6	2

P50 Remaining remainders

1 12 months, £3 change.
2 4 books, £4 left.
3 18 boxes, one with only one tube in it.
4 6 piles, 6 extra chairs.
5 6 packs of 4, 1 left.
6 £2.60 each, none left over.

P53 Close enough?

1 610 + 290.
2 20 × 7 or 2 × 10 × 7.
3 100 – 70.
4 350 – 100.
5 1000 + 10.
6 5 × 10 × 5.

P55 Equivalence snap

The equivalent fractions are:
½, $^{2}/_{4}$, $^{8}/_{16}$ and $^{4}/_{8}$
¼ and $^{2}/_{8}$
$^{1}/_{5}$ and $^{2}/_{10}$
$^{1}/_{8}$ and $^{2}/_{16}$
$^{1}/_{10}$ and $^{2}/_{20}$

Answer sheet

P56 Favourite days
1 100
2 Wednesday
3 Thursday
4 30
6 9

Summer term

P62 Beat the clock

4	2	8
68	66	32
64	5	65
7	15	48
7	39	82
66	59	42
36	64	

P63 Column skills

494	251	188
676	716	922

P64 Subtracting columns

56	219	149
479	657	866

P72 Multiple magic
6 15
90 60
12, 24, 36, 48
52, 56, 60, 64, 68, 72, 76
60 15
90

P73 Dividing codes
Divisible by 2 and 3: 6, 12, 18, 24, 30, 36, 60, 72, 78, 90.
Divisible by 2 and 5: 20, 30, 40, 60, 70, 80, 90, 100, 160.
Divisible by 3 and 4: 12, 24, 36, 60, 72.
Divisible by 4 and 5: 20, 40, 60, 80, 100, 160.

P74 Matching sentences
2: 1 x 1 x 2.
6: 2 x 3; 2 x 3 x 1; 3 x 2; 2 x 3; 3 x 2 x 1; 1 x 2 x 3.
12: 3 x 2 x 2; 2 x 2 x 3; 2 x 3 x 2.
18: 2 x 3 x 3; 3 x 3 x 2.
24: 4 x 2 x 3; 2 x 3 x 4; 3 x 2 x 4; 4 x 3 x 2.
25: 5 x 5 x 1; 5 x 5.
42: 7 x 6 x 1; 7 x 6; 6 x 7.
56: 7 x 1 x 8; 7 x 8; 8 x 7 x 1.

P76 Higher or lower?
Less than $\frac{1}{2}$: $\frac{1}{4}$, $\frac{1}{3}$, $\frac{1}{5}$, $\frac{1}{10}$, $\frac{3}{8}$, 0.25, 0.1, 0.01.
More than $\frac{1}{2}$: $\frac{2}{3}$, 0.75, $\frac{3}{4}$, $\frac{7}{10}$, $\frac{9}{10}$, $\frac{4}{5}$, $\frac{7}{8}$, 0.6, 1.25, 2.5, 10.1.

P77 Decimals equal fractions
Mineral water and olive oil (7.5 litres).
Vinegar and large cook-in sauce (0.75 litres).
Soy sauce and brown sauce (0.25 pints).
Herbs and chilli powder (2.5 grams).
Milk and orange juice (2.5 pints).
Toothpaste and wasp sting cream (3.5 oz).
Mayonnaise and black bean stir-in sauce (250 grams).
Lip balm and lens cleaner (2.25 grams).

P78 Trans-Air challenge
1 1 hour 35 minutes
2 Yes
3 No
4 Thursday
5 5 minutes
6 3 hours 15 minutes
7 14.10

P79 Money columns
£13.56 + £8.76 = £22.32
£13.56 + £6.78 = £20.34
£13.56 + £3.14 = £16.70
£13.56 + £2.99 = £16.55
£13.56 + £8.12 = £21.68
£8.76 + £6.78 = £15.54
£8.76 + £3.14 = £11.90
£8.76 + £2.99 = £11.75
£8.76 + £8.12 = £16.88
£6.78 + £3.14 = £9.92
£6.78 + £2.99 = £9.77
£6.78 + £8.12 = £14.90
£3.14 + £2.99 = £6.13
£3.14 + £8.12 = £11.26
£2.99 + £8.12 = £11.11

P81 Workout pictograms

☺ = 10 children

Hours	Number of children
Less than 1 hour	☺
Less than 2 hours	☺☺
Less than 3 hours	☺☺☺◐
Less than 4 hours	☺◐
4 hours or more	☺☺

HOMEWORK

Year 4 Key objectives

a Use symbols correctly, including less than (<), greater than (>), equals (=).
b Round any positive integer less than 1000 to the nearest 10 or 100.
c Recognise simple fractions that are several parts of a whole, and mixed numbers; recognise the equivalence of simple fractions.
d Use known number facts and place value to add or subtract mentally, including any pair of two-digit whole numbers.
e Carry out column addition and subtraction of two integers less than 1000, and column addition of more than two such integers.
f Know by heart facts for the 2, 3, 4, 5 and 10 multiplication tables.
g Derive quickly division facts corresponding to the 2, 3, 4, 5 and 10 multiplication tables.
h Find remainders after division.
i Know and use the relationships between familiar units of length, mass and capacity.
j Classify polygons, using criteria such as number of right angles, whether or not they are regular, symmetry properties.
k Choose and use appropriate number operations and ways of calculating (mental, mental with jottings, pencil and paper) to solve problems.

Introduction

The planning for the assessment units is based upon the NNS medium-term plans. There is an assessment unit for each end of half-term, as well as end-of-year assessments. Each unit consists of two detailed lesson plans, each assessing one of the key objectives, with an accompanying photocopiable activity sheet for each lesson. The notes include suggestions for further work where children have not met the objective. There are additional oral and mental, practical and written activities covering the range of key objectives taught that half-term, with photocopiable assessment sheets for written work. For the end-of-year assessment there is an assessment covering all the Year 4 key objectives, a mental assessment and a written assessment. The end-of-year assessments mirror the style of the national tests or QCA non-statutory tests. Letters alongside each objective (see left) appear alongside each assessment activity to help you identify which objectives are covered by each activity.

Using the assessment units

Choose the half-term assessment that matches your planning needs. From your ongoing teacher assessments, identify the children who you believe have achieved specific key objectives. Now decide upon the children who you suspect may have met the key objective/s but for whom you have no firm assessment data (a class record sheet has been provided on page 141 for this purpose). These children can form the target group for assessment; arrange for them to work with an adult during practical activities, who should use the probing questions included in the assessment notes for teachers. Ask all the children to complete the written assessments, putting the probing questions to the targeted group.

Supporting teaching assistants

Provide the teaching assistant with details of the activity (whether practical or written). Discuss the probing questions to be used and how responses will be recorded. Did the child give appropriate, correct responses to the questions? Was a specific question answered inappropriately? Where the latter occurs, some additional notes about what the child failed to understand would be helpful for planning future teaching. Discuss the outcomes of the assessment activity together, and make notes about individual children.

Assessment for learning

Assessment is always for a purpose – here it is to check what individual children understand, know and can do, and where they need further teaching in order to achieve the key objectives. Use the outcomes of the assessment for forward planning for teaching and for homework provision. The *All New 100 Maths Lessons* series provides detailed planning grids for each term, which can be used to identify further activities to support those who need more experiences in particular topics.

Assess and Review

Key objectives to be assessed

Assessment lesson 1: **Classify polygons, using criteria such as number of right angles, whether or not they are regular, symmetry properties.**
Assessment lesson 2: **Choose and use appropriate number operations and ways of calculating (mental, mental with jottings, pencil and paper) to solve problems.**

Photocopiable pages
Shape tile (p87); Word problems (p89); Question allsorts (p90); Assessment test (p91-92).

Equipment
Individual whiteboards and pens; scissors.

Assessment Activities

Mental maths assessment

Know and use the relationships between familiar units of length i

Ask the children to write on their whiteboards the shortened form of units you name. When you say 'Show me', they hold up their boards for you to see. Say, for example: *centimetre, millimetre, kilometre, metre.* Now repeat the exercise, this time asking the children to write out the word, rather than the shortened form.

Probing questions

- *How many metres is 200 centimetres?*
- *How many millimetres are there in 5 centimetres?*
- *How many metres is 1½ kilometres?*

Written maths assessment

Provide each child with a copy of the 'Question allsorts' activity sheet and check that they understand what to do for each part of the sheet. You can ask all the children in the class to complete this sheet and then ask small, targeted groups of children, whose progress you are unsure about, the probing questions listed below. Alternatively, you can work with a targeted group and use the probing questions as the children work through the sheet.

Probing questions

1. Choose and use appropriate number operations and ways of calculating (mental, mental with jottings, pencil and paper) to solve problems k

- *How do you know whether to add, subtract, multiply or divide?*
- *Can you make up a word problem that can be solved with this calculation: 6 x 3 + 4?*

2. Carry out column addition of two integers less than 1000, and column addition of more than two such integers e

- *How can you estimate the answer?*
- *How can you check that the answer is correct?*

3. Classify polygons, using criteria such as number of right angles, whether or not they are regular, symmetry properties j

- *Draw an irregular polygon.*
- *Name three regular polygons.*

Shape tile

Key objective:
Classify polygons, using criteria such as number of right angles, whether or not they are regular, symmetry properties.

What you need
- A copy of the 'Shape tile' activity sheet for each pair of children; an enlarged A3 copy of 'Shape tile', with the shapes cut out; individual whiteboards and pens; scissors.

Further support
If possible, ask an adult to work with the less able children. The activity can begin with the adult choosing a shape and the children taking turns to ask a question. Do not limit the number of questions. Ask the adult to help the children to phrase their questions so that a yes or no answer is possible. When the children are confident with this they can work in pairs in the same way as the other children, but without the limit on the number of questions.

Oral and mental starter
Explain that you will say the name of a shape. Ask the children to sketch that shape quickly. When you say 'Show me', the children hold up their boards for you to check. Say, for example: *Sketch a square ... a rectangle ... a quadrilateral with one right angle ... a hexagon.*

Main assessment activity
Choose one of the large shapes and hide it from the children. Ask them to think of questions about the shapes that can be answered only by yes or no. Allow the children to question you until someone works out what shape you are hiding. If any of the questions cannot be answered by yes or no, invite the children to re-phrase the question so that you can answer it.

Ask the children to work in pairs. Explain that they will need to cut out their shape tiles quickly and shuffle them, placing them in a stack. They take turns to take the top card, hiding it from their partner. Now their partner asks questions that can only be answered with yes or no. Tell the children that they can ask only ten questions and if they guess the shape correctly they win a point. The children can keep a log of points won on a piece of paper.

As the children work, target individuals who you are not yet sure have achieved the key objective. Listen to the questions they ask, checking that they understand the vocabulary of shape and know the properties of the shapes.

Plenary
Play the game again, this time with the class split into two teams, with a captain for each. The captains take it in turns to pick up a shape and hide it from view. Their team then asks them ten questions. If the team has not guessed the shape after ten questions the other team takes over. Explain that each child can only ask one question per shape, so that everyone has a turn at phrasing a question. Ask probing questions such as:
- *Can you name a shape that is also a polygon?*
- *Tell me a shape that is not a polygon.*
- *Tell me one of your shapes that is a polygon and has at least one line of symmetry.*

Shape tile

- Work with a partner.
- Cut out these shape tiles.
  - Shuffle the tiles.
  - Take turns to pick up a tile. Do not show your partner which one you have.
  - Your partner will ask you up to ten questions about the shapes.
  - You can answer Yes or No.
- If your partner guesses the shape you are holding they score a point.

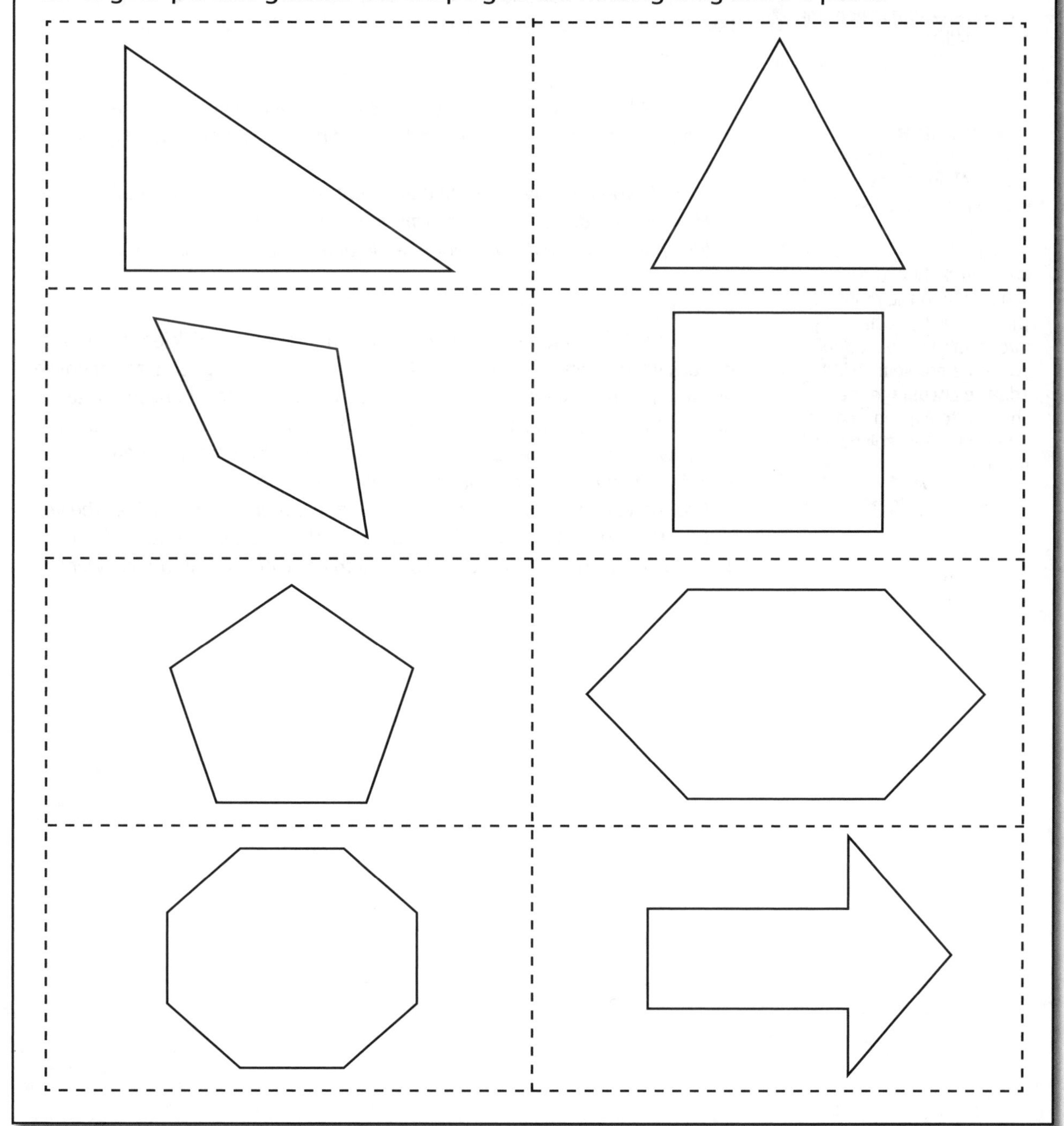

Word problems

Key objective:
Choose and use appropriate number operations and ways of calculating (mental, mental with jottings, pencil and paper) to solve problems.

What you need

- A copy of the 'Word problems' activity sheet for each child.

Further support

You may wish to simplify the numbers in the problems for the less able children. Ask an adult to work with this group, if possible, to help the children read the problem, then to discuss what information is needed to solve the problem. Ask the adult to encourage the children to explain to each other how they solved each problem.

Oral and mental starter

Explain that you will ask a word problem and would like the children to work out the answer. Say, for example: *Paul bought 180 marbles, then gave half of these to his brother. How many marbles did he have left?* (90) *How did you work that out?* Repeat with other word problems, such as: *Eve had 130 stickers. She was given another 80 stickers by her uncle. Then she gave half of her stickers to her sister. How many has she now?* (105)

Main assessment activity

Explain to the children that you will give them an activity sheet with some word problems to solve. Ask them to work through these on their own. Allow about 15 minutes for this and then ask the children to discuss with a partner how they worked out their solutions. Allow about ten minutes for this discussion.

As the children work, concentrate on those for whom you need more information about their ability to solve word problems. Ask probing questions such as:

- *How do you know whether to add ... subtract ... multiply ... divide?*
- *How did you decide which information you needed?*
- *Which information did you not need in order to answer this question?*

Plenary

Leave about 15 minutes for the Plenary so that there is sufficient time to discuss each question. Invite a child that you are targeting for assessment to explain how they solved the first question. Discuss whether anyone used a different method, and which method the children thought was easier to use and why. Repeat this for the second question. For the third question, ask:

- *How did you work out which information you needed?*
- *How do you know how many books there were on the middle/top shelves?*
- *Was there any information in the problem that you did not need?* (No)
- *What sort of calculations did you need to carry out to find the answer?*

Name Date

Word problems

- Decide how to work out the answers to each of these questions.
- Show your jottings.

Problem	Jottings	Your answer
1. David had 150 marbles. Jack gave him 40 blue marbles and a book for his birthday. David bought another 30 red marbles. How many marbles has David altogether?		
2. Clare eats a yoghurt every day. Her favourite yoghurt is strawberry. How many yoghurts will she eat in six weeks?		
3. Gary counted the books on the shelves in the classroom. He worked out that on the top shelf there were twice as many books as on the middle shelf. The bottom shelf had 35 books, which was 15 less than the middle shelf. How many books were there altogether?		

Name Date

Question allsorts

- Write the answer to this number sentence: 425 + 164 = ____________
- Write your jottings in the space below.

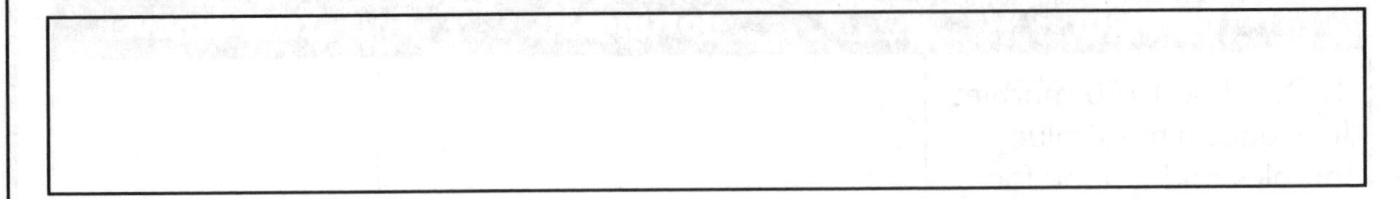

- Now write a word problem for the above number sentence:

____

- Use column addition to write the answers to these addition problems.

$$\begin{array}{r} 145 \\ +\ 87 \\ \hline \end{array} \qquad \begin{array}{r} 354 \\ +\ 78 \\ \hline \end{array} \qquad \begin{array}{r} 626 \\ +\ 53 \\ \hline \end{array}$$

- Draw a shape for each section of this Carroll diagram.

	Triangles	Not triangles
Regular		
Irregular		

Name Date

Assessment 1

1. Write these measurements in words.

cm ______________________

km ______________________

mm ______________________

m ______________________

2. Use column addition to work out the answers to these addition sentences.

	1	6	9	+	8	7			4	3	7	+	5	8	
	2	6	4	+	7	6			4	4	4	+	7	8	

Name Date

3. Sketch these shapes:

Irregular pentagon with one right-angled vertex	Quadrilateral with one right-angled vertex	A four-sided shape with four lines of symmetry

4. Work out the answers to these number sentences:

6 x 4 = ______

156 + 77 = ______

5. Write word problems to fit the number sentences.

______

______

______

______

Assess and Review

Key objectives to be assessed
Assessment lesson 1: **Recognise simple fractions that are several parts of a whole, and mixed numbers; recognise the equivalence of simple fractions.**
Assessment lesson 2: **Carry out column subtraction of two integers less than 1000.**

Photocopiable pages
Fraction cards (p94); Find the difference (p97); What is missing? (p98); Assessment test (p99-100).

Equipment
Individual whiteboards and pens; paper; Blu-Tack; scissors; 0-9 numeral cards.

Assessment Activities

Mental maths assessment
Recognise simple fractions that are several parts of a whole, and mixed numbers; recognise the equivalence of simple fractions c
Draw an empty number line on the board, labelled 0 at one end and 1 at the other. Invite individual children to take a fraction card and place it where they think it fits on the number line. Repeat this until all the cards are placed. Discuss where the equivalent fractions fit, such as ½ and ²/₄.
Probing questions
- *Tell me some fractions that are equivalent to ½ ... ¼ ... ¾ ... ¹/₃ ... ²/₃ and so on.*
- *Tell me some fractions that are less than ½. How do you know?*

Written maths assessment
Provide each child with a copy of the 'What is missing?' activity sheet and check that they understand what to do for each part. You can ask the whole class to complete this sheet. If you do this you can then ask the probing questions of small targeted groups of children whose progress against the key objectives you are unsure of. Alternatively, you can work with a targeted group and use the probing questions as the children work.
Probing questions
As they work, ask individuals:
1. Choose and use appropriate number operations and ways of calculating (mental, mental with jottings, pencil and paper) to solve problems k
- *How do you know which operation to choose?*

2. Carry out column subtraction of two integers less than 1000 e
- *What tips would you give someone to help them with column subtraction?*
- *How can you check if the answer to this is correct?*

Fraction cards

Key objective:
Recognise simple fractions that are several parts of a whole, and mixed numbers; recognise the equivalence of simple fractions.

What you need
- A copy of the 'Fraction cards' activity sheet for each pair; A3 enlargement (cut up) of 'Fraction cards'; Blu-Tack fixed to the back of each teaching card; a pair of scissors for each pair; individual whiteboards and pens; paper rectangles cut to the same size as the cards on the 'Fraction cards' activity sheet.

Further support
After the less able children have played Snap, decide whether to limit them to unitary fractions, such as $\frac{1}{2}$, $\frac{1}{3}$, $\frac{1}{4}$, $\frac{1}{5}$ and $\frac{1}{10}$. Ask them to find at least one equivalent fraction for each of their unitary fractions.

Oral and mental starter
Explain that you will say a fraction. Ask the children to write the fraction on their whiteboards, using numerals, and when you say 'Show me' they hold up their boards. Begin with fractions such as $\frac{1}{2}$, $\frac{1}{4}$ and $\frac{1}{3}$, then move to fractions that are several parts of a whole, such as $\frac{4}{5}$ and $\frac{3}{10}$.

Main assessment activity
Using the enlarged cards from 'Fraction cards', choose a unitary fraction, such as $\frac{1}{2}$, and ask the children to suggest another fraction that is equivalent to this. Write on the board several suggestions that they make, such as $\frac{2}{4}$, $\frac{4}{8}$, $\frac{3}{6}$.

Ask the children to work in pairs. Give each pair a copy of 'Fraction cards' and a pair of scissors. Ask them to cut out quickly the fraction cards from the activity sheet. Explain that you would like them to spend about five minutes playing Snap with the cards. As they do this, check that the children you are targeting for assessment recognise the equivalent fractions.

After five minutes, ask the children to listen carefully. Provide each pair with several pieces of rectangular paper. Explain that first of all you would like them to sort out their cards into sets of equivalent fractions. Then ask them to choose one of their fraction cards and to agree two more fractions that are equivalent to their chosen fraction. They write each one on a piece of paper. Ask them to repeat this for each set of fraction cards that they have. Again, as the children work, check that the children you are targeting for assessment can find equivalent fractions.

Plenary
Explain that you would like the children to work in two teams, and that the team captains will take turns to say a fraction. The children quickly write an equivalent fraction on their whiteboards. The teams take turns to hold up their boards and the captain counts the number of different equivalent fractions that their team has written. Then the other team captain does the same. The team with more different, equivalent fractions wins that round. Play the game for a few rounds, then ask some probing questions, choosing the children you are targeting for assessment to respond. Ask, for example:
- *Tell me another fraction that is equivalent to...*
- *Say some fractions that are greater than $\frac{1}{2}$. How can you tell?*
- *Say some fractions greater than 1.*

Fraction cards

- Photocopy this sheet onto card and cut out the fraction cards.

$\frac{1}{4}$	$\frac{2}{8}$	$\frac{2}{4}$
$\frac{4}{16}$	$\frac{3}{12}$	$\frac{4}{8}$
$\frac{8}{32}$	$\frac{1}{32}$	$\frac{6}{12}$
$\frac{3}{6}$	$\frac{5}{10}$	$\frac{1}{2}$

Find the difference

Key objective:
Carry out column subtraction of two integers less than 1000.

What you need
- A copy of the 'Find the difference' activity sheet for each child; individual whiteboards and pens; two sets of 0-9 numeral cards for each pair.

Further support
Decide whether to limit the less able children to TU - TU questions, using just four numeral cards each time. If possible, ask an adult to work with the less able children. Ask the children to take turns to explain how to work out the answer. Ask the adult to encourage them to use the appropriate vocabulary of subtraction, modelling responses if necessary.

Oral and mental starter

Explain that you will ask a subtraction question. Ask the children to write their answer onto their whiteboards, and, when you say 'Show me', the children hold up their board for you to see. Say, for example, *What is the difference between 15 and 8? How many more is 19 than 7? What is 2004 minus 7? What is 74 subtract19?*

Main assessment activity

Invite a child to take the top three numeral cards from a stack and arrange them into a HTU number. Write this number on the board. Now ask another child to take another two cards and to arrange these as a TU number. Write this, correctly placed, under the HTU number, and put in the subtraction sign, so that it makes a column subtraction sentence. Ask the children to copy down the number sentence and calculate the answer. Discuss how they did this, and check that everyone is using the column subtraction, counting-up method.

Now ask the children to work in pairs. Provide each child with a copy of the 'Find the difference' activity sheet. Explain that you would like them to take turns to choose five numeral cards, and to make a HTU and a TU number. They set these out as a column subtraction and, using the counting-up method, work out the answer. Ask them to repeat this nine more times.

While they work, concentrate on the children you are targeting for assessment. Ask probing questions, such as:
- *How do you know you have the correct answer?*
- *How could you check your answer?*

Plenary

Invite pairs of children to set one of their HTU - TU sentences for others to try. Discuss how they worked this out. Repeat this for several different questions. Now ask the children to explain how they could check that the answer is correct. Invite a child to write on the board to demonstrate their method. For example, they might use addition or a number line subtraction method for checking. Where a mistake is made, invite the children to explain what is wrong and how to correct it.

Name Date

Find the difference

- Work with a partner.
- You will need two sets of 0–9 numeral cards.
  - Shuffle the cards and place them into a stack.
  - Take turns to take five cards.
  - Make a HTU number and a TU number.
  - Both of you write a column subtraction sentence.
  - Work out the answer by using the counting-up method
- Do this nine more times.

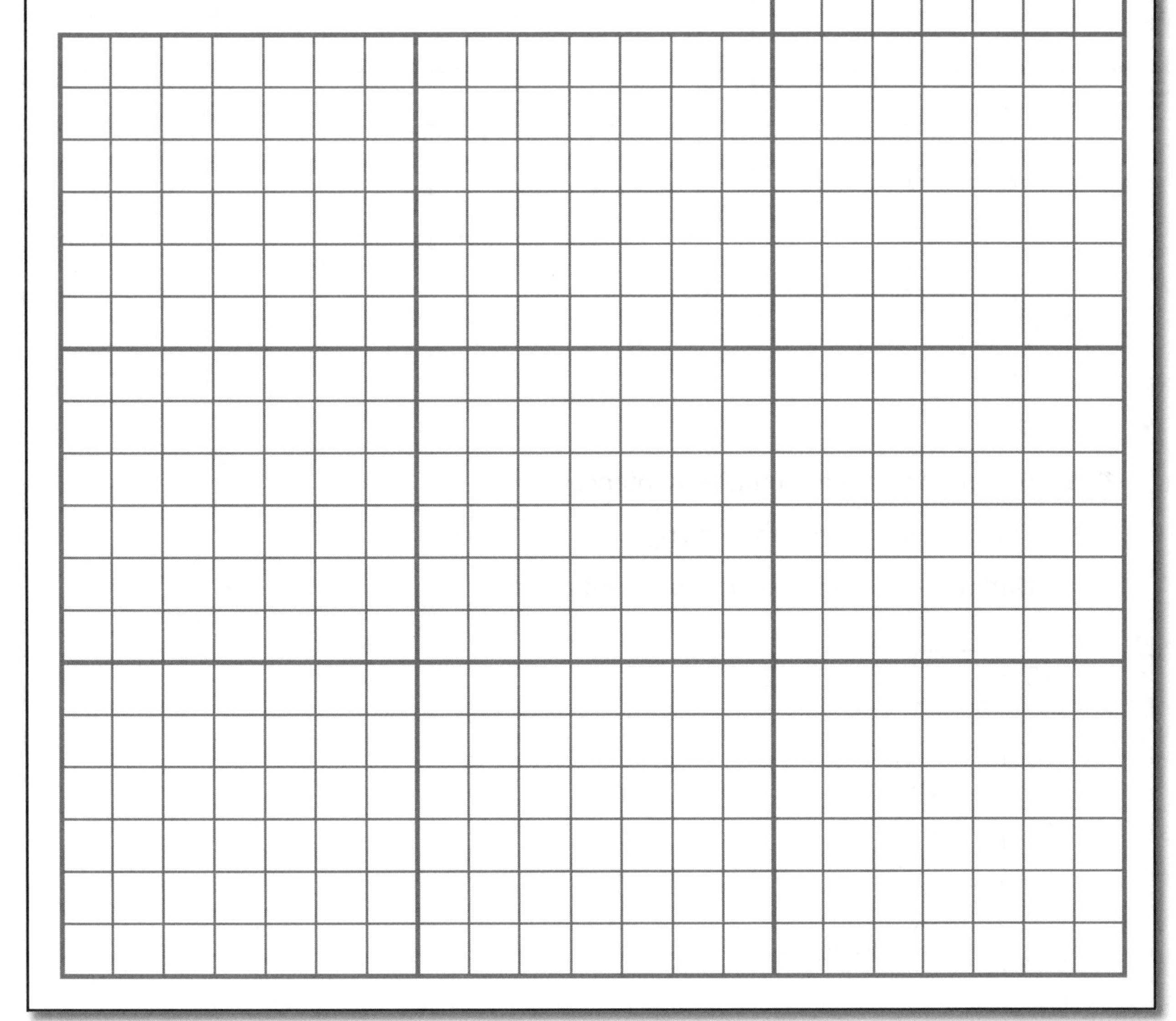

Name Date

What is missing?

- Find the answers to these subtraction sentences.
  - Write the sentences again in columns.
  - Use the counting-up method.

345 – 86 975 – 78 444 – 89 406 – 77

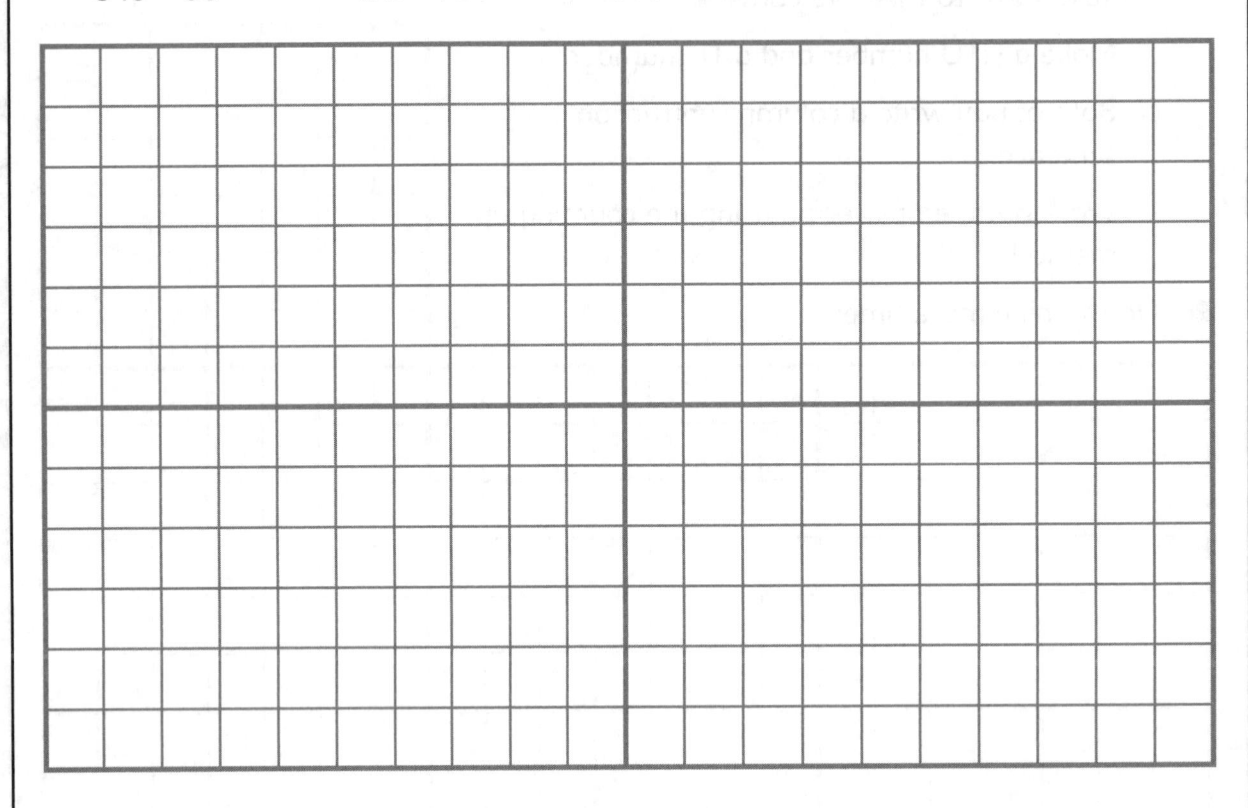

- Look carefully at these number sentences.
  - The operation signs are missing.
  - Decide which operation it is and write it in.

45 ☐ 5 = 225

72 ☐ 6 = 12

142 ☐ 89 = 231

699 ☐ 300 = 399

Name Date

Assessment 2

1. Write the fraction for the shaded part of the shape.

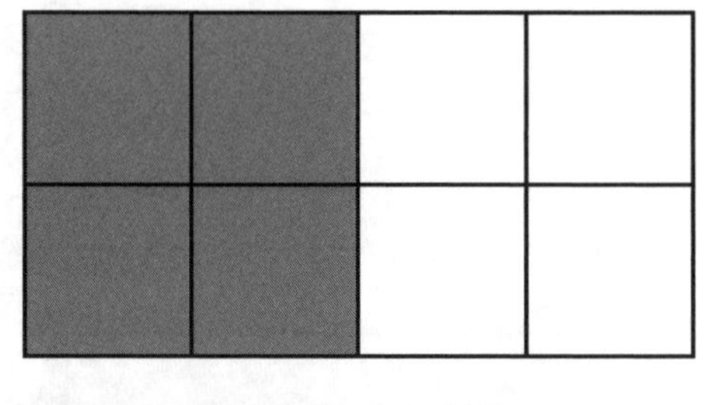

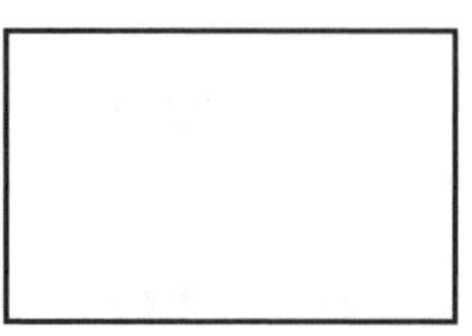

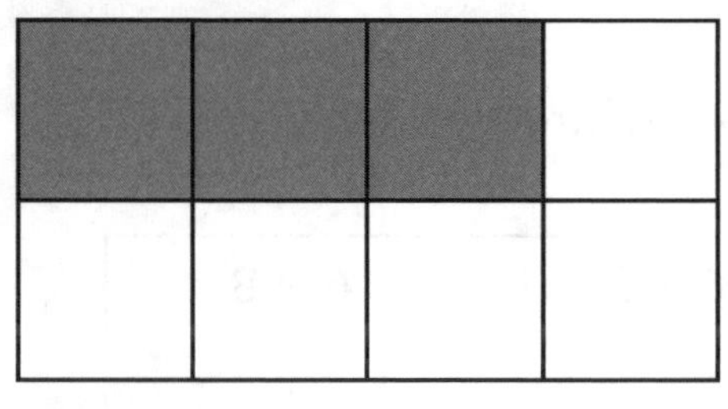

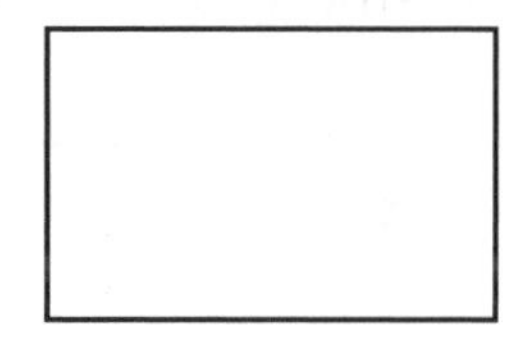

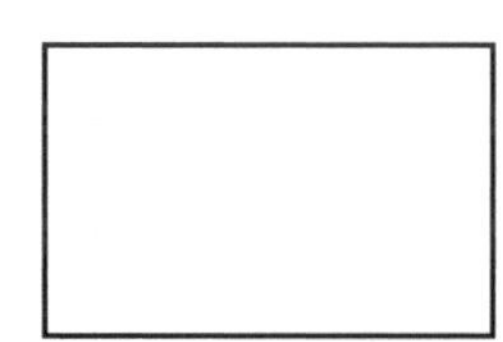

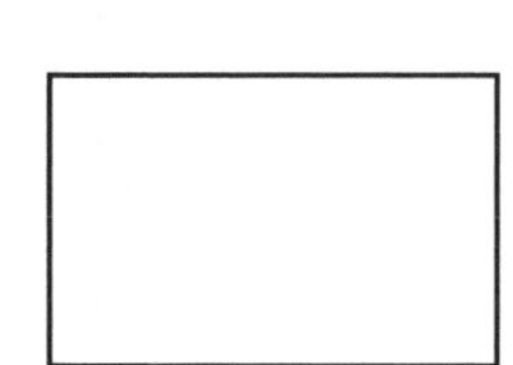

2. Write a fraction that is worth the same:

$\frac{2}{4}$ 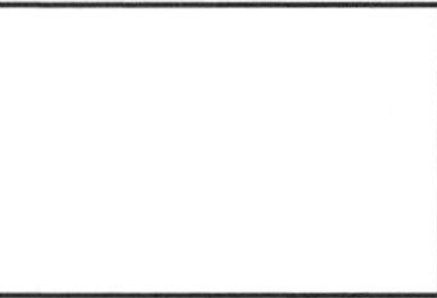

$\frac{5}{10}$ 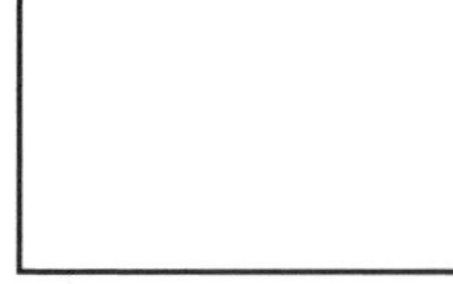

$\frac{4}{6}$ 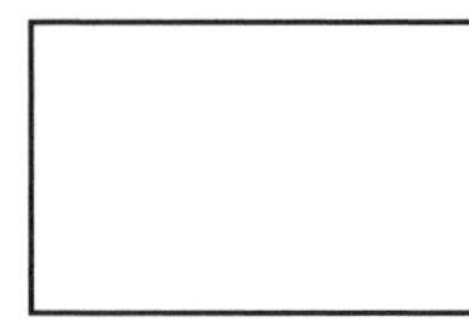

$\frac{6}{8}$ 

Name Date

3. Write the missing operation signs in these number sentences.

45 [ ] 5 = 9

6 [ ] 3 = 18

8004 [ ] 7 = 7997

56 [ ] 81 = 137

4. Use the counting-up method to work out these subtraction sentences.

		4	5	6	–	8	7				6	3	1	–	6	8	
		2	0	8	–	6	9				5	5	5	–	7	7	

Assess and Review

Key objectives to be assessed

Assessment lesson 1: **Know and use the relationships between familiar units of length and mass.**

Assessment lesson 2: **Know by heart facts for the 2, 3, 4, 5 and 10 multiplication tables.**

Photocopiable pages

Length and mass (p103); Multiplication table facts (p105); Using numbers (p106); Assessment test (p107-108).

Equipment

Individual whiteboards and pens.

Mental maths assessment

Know by heart facts for the 2, 3, 4, 5 and 10 multiplication tables f

Explain that you will ask the children some 2, 3, 4, 5 and 10 times-tables facts. Ask them to record their answers quickly on their whiteboards, and when you say 'Show me', they hold up their boards for you to see. Ask, for example: *What is 5 multiplied by 2? What is the product of 6 and 4? What must I multiply 10 by to get an answer of 90?*

Probing questions

- *How many different multiplication facts can you tell me with the number 12 in them?*
- *How many different division facts do you know which have the number 12 in them?*

Written maths assessment

Provide each child with a copy of the 'Using numbers' activity sheet and check that they understand what to do for each part of the sheet. You can ask all the children in the class to complete this sheet and then ask small, targeted groups of children, whose progress you are unsure about, the probing questions listed below. Alternatively, you can work with a targeted group and use the probing questions as the children work through the sheet.

Probing questions

1. Use symbols correctly, including less than (<), greater than (>), equals (=) a

- *What could the missing sign be?*
- *How did you work that out?*

2. Round any positive integer less than 1000 to the nearest 10 or 100 b

- *I rounded a number to the nearest 10. The answer is 540. What could I have started with?*

3. Choose and use appropriate number operations and ways of calculating (mental, mental with jottings, pencil and paper) to solve problems k

- *Which number operation did you need to use?*
- *How did you know to use that operation?*

4. Know and use the relationships between familiar units of length and mass i

- *Can you tell me another way to write 3km? ... 2000m? ... 5000g?*

Length and mass

Key objective:
Know and use the relationships between familiar units of length and mass.

What you need
- A copy of the 'Length and mass' activity sheet for each child; an A3 enlargement of 'Length and mass'.

Further support
Ask an adult to work with less able children. They can use an A3 enlargement of the activity sheet, pinned to a flipchart. Ask the adult to encourage the children to give responses to the questions in sentences, using the vocabulary of length and mass.

Oral and mental starter

Explain that you will write the shortened form of a measurement on the board. Ask the children to write the complete word on their whiteboards. When you say 'Show me', they hold these up for you to see. Write **mm**, **cm**, **m** and **km**, which children covered in the autumn term, then **g** and **kg**.

Main assessment activity

Pin up an A3 copy of the activity sheet 'Length and mass'. Invite the children to suggest where they might use centimetres when measuring, and show them where to write their responses to question 1 on the sheet. Explain that the question asks them to think of three occasions on which they could use each unit of measure listed. Read through the other questions on the list and check that the children know where to write their responses.

While the children are working, target those for whom you need further assessment data. Ask probing questions, such as:
- *Would you rather have 260g of sweets or ¼ kg of sweets?*
- *Which is longer, 450 centimetres or 5 metres?*

Plenary

Review the activity sheet together, using the A3 enlargement of the sheet. Invite the children to suggest at least ten items to go into each of the boxes in question 1, and to try to think of different things from those they have already listed on their sheet.

Invite the children to suggest some measures of length, such as 3½ metres or 550 centimetres. Write their suggestions on sheets of paper and invite some children to stand at the front of the class, holding these sheets. Invite the other children to order them, from smallest to largest. Repeat for weights.

Write 3km on the board and ask: *How else could I write this?* Agree that it could be written as 3000m. Repeat for other measures.

Length and mass

- In each box, write three things that you would measure using the units at the top of the box.

Kilogram	Gram	Kilometre
Metre	**Centimetre**	**Millimetre**

- Complete this table:

1 kilometre = ☐ metres

1 metre = ☐ centimetres

1 centimetre = ☐ millimetres

1 kilogram = ☐ grams

- Write these measurements using the second set of units.

$1\frac{1}{2}$ metres	centimetres
5 kilograms	grams
6 kilometres	metres
2500 grams	kilograms
60 centimetres	millimetres
250 centimetres	metres

- Underline the measurement that you think would be correct for each of these.

☐ A bungalow is about: 3 metres 6 metres 11 metres tall.

☐ An orange weighs about: 10g 150g 1500g.

☐ My little finger is about: 8mm 18mm 28mm wide.

☐ The length of the garage is about: 2 metres 7 metres 20 metres.

Multiplication table facts

Key objective:
Know by heart facts for the 2, 3, 4, 5 and 10 multiplication tables.

What you need
- A copy of the 'Multiplication table facts' activity sheet for each pair; A3 enlargement of 'Multiplication table facts'; individual whiteboards and pens.

Further support
Decide whether to concentrate on, say, the 2, 5 and 10 times-tables facts with less able children. Ask an adult to work with these children. The adult writes a product from these tables on the board, then the children write the multiplication sentence on their whiteboards and hold these up when the adult asks them to. Ask the adult to encourage the children to say the complete multiplication sentence each time.

Oral and mental starter

Explain that you will say an 'answer' to a multiplication in the 2, 3, 4, 5 or 10 times-table. Ask the children to suggest what the question was. Encourage them to phrase their responses in different ways, using vocabulary such as multiplication, product, times. Keep the pace sharp to encourage rapid recall of the facts.

Main assessment activity

Pin up the enlarged copy of the 'Multiplication table facts' activity sheet. Point to the number 12 on the grid and ask: *What table fact can you think of that has that number as its answer?* Ask the children to suggest some more multiplications. Make a list on the board of their responses: 6 × 2; 2 × 6; 3 × 4; 4 × 3. Ask: *Does every product have lots of different multiples?* Agree that for each number on the grid there are at least two possible responses, but not every number will have more than two.

Ask the children to work in pairs, with a copy of the activity sheet between them. They must decide who will write a tick and who a cross. One child then chooses a number from the grid. Their partner says a multiplication sentence with the chosen number as the product. If they agree that this is correct, the child who said the number sentence writes their mark (tick or cross) over the chosen number. They repeat this, taking it in turns to choose a number, until all the numbers in the grid have been ticked or crossed. The children count the number of ticks or crosses to see who has won the game.

Observe the children you are targeting for assessment. Check that they have quick recall of the number facts. Note any multiplication tables where the children falter, as further practice will be needed with these facts to commit them to memory.

Plenary

Using the A3 enlargement of the activity sheet again, divide the class into two teams, each with a team captain. One team can be tick and the other cross. Play the game again, this time with the team captains choosing the number for the opposing team. Each child can only be chosen once, and the game is over when everyone in the team has had a turn. Encourage the children to play the game at a good pace, so that they recall the number facts quickly.

Now ask some probing questions, such as:
- *If the product is 20, what could the multiple be?*
- *What division facts can you think of that use the number 20?*
- *Now let's try this again with the number 24.*

Name Date

Multiplication table facts

- Work with a partner.
  - One of you will use ✔ the other ✘.
  - Take turns to choose a number from the grid.
  - Ask your partner to say a multiplication fact that includes your chosen number.
  - If you agree, your partner can put their mark (tick or cross) over that number.
  - When all the numbers have been marked, count up the ticks and the crosses.
- The winner is the player who has more questions correct.

2	45	80	32	24	12	15	16	10	30
36	27	90	12	60	18	25	24	6	30
30	8	40	16	20	10	28	8	3	5
40	10	15	20	21	20	35	40	4	50
18	20	4	12	50	15	70	6	9	100

Name Date

Using numbers

- Use the symbols <, > and = to make these number equations true.

556 ☐ 372

123 ☐ 456

169 + 20 ☐ 100 + 89

503 – 8 ☐ 490 + 5

- Round these numbers to the nearest 10.

556 ________

879 ________

424 ________

307 ________

- Round these numbers to the nearest 100.

890 ________

705 ________

663 ________

829 ________

- Write the answers to these word problems. Write your jottings.

  - ☐ Felip had 5kg of white flour and 6kg of brown flour. How many grams of flour did he have in total?

  - ☐ Marisa measured how much ribbon she had. She had 2 metres of red ribbon and 5 metres of red ribbon. How many centimetres of ribbon did she have altogether?

Name Date

Assessment 3

1. Write a different multiplication for each number sentence

☐	x	☐	=	20
☐	x	☐	=	20
☐	x	☐	=	20
☐	x	☐	=	20
☐	x	☐	=	40
☐	x	☐	=	40
☐	x	☐	=	40
☐	x	☐	=	40

2. Write the missing symbols in these number sentences.
Use <, > or = .

907	–	8	☐	800	+	99
732	+	50	☐	632	+	200
60	x	10	☐	500	–	50
100	+	500	☐	750	–	150

3. Write the units for these measurements.

The garden was 100 ________ in length.

The chicken weighed 2 ________.

The baby measured 53 ________. long.

The apple weighed 75 ________.

Name Date

4. Write the answers to these word problems.

□ Write your jottings.

There is 500g of sugar in the bag. Each cake needs 150g of sugar. How many cakes can we bake? How much sugar will be left over?

There were 2kg of potatoes, 500g of carrots and 1250g of onions in the vegetable basket. The cook removed 250g of onions. In grams, what do the vegetables in the basket weigh now?

The children laid their scarves out on the ground, end to end. Mark's scarf was 120cm long, Jed's scarf was 95cm in length, Jo's scarf was 110cm long and Dilshad's scarf was 150cm long. In metres, how long were the scarves in total?

Paul walked 18km. Then he travelled by bus for 75km. He took the train and travelled another 250km. How far did he travel in total?

Assess and Review

Key objectives to be assessed

Assessment lesson 1: **Derive quickly division facts corresponding to the 2, 3, 4, 5 and 10 multiplication tables.**
Assessment lesson 2: **Find remainders after division.**

Photocopiable pages
Division (p111); Remainders (p113); Word problems (p114); Assessment test (p115-116).

Equipment
Individual whiteboards and pens; 0-9 numeral cards.

Assessment Activities

Mental maths assessment

Derive quickly division facts corresponding to the 2, 3, 4, 5 and 10 multiplication tables g

Explain that you will ask some division questions, which the children can derive from their knowledge of the 2, 3, 4, 5 and 10 times-tables. Ask the children to raise their hands to answer. Keep the pace sharp. Ask, for instance: *What is 15 divided by 5? Can you tell me another division sentence that begins with 15? How many 10s are there in 90?*

Written maths assessment

Provide each child with a copy of the 'Word problems' activity sheet and check that they understand what to do for each part. You can ask the whole class to complete this sheet. If you do this you can then ask the probing questions of small, targeted groups of children whose progress against the key objectives you are unsure of. Alternatively, you can work with a targeted group and use the probing questions as the children work.

Probing questions

1. Find remainders after division h

- *Do all divisions have remainders? Why not?*
- *Tell me a divisions sentence with a remainder of 3.*

2. Choose and use appropriate number operations and ways of calculating (mental, mental with jottings, pencil and paper) to solve problems k

- *How do you know whether to add, subtract, multiply or divide?*
- *What are important things to remember when solving word problems?*

3. Recognise simple fractions that are several parts of a whole, and mixed numbers; recognise the equivalence of simple fractions c

- *Tell me some fractions that are equivalent to ½ ... $^1/_4$ ... $^1/_3$ ... $^1/_5$.*
- *How do you know?*

Division

Key objective:
Derive quickly division facts corresponding to the 2, 3, 4, 5 and 10 multiplication tables.

What you need
- A copy of the 'Division' activity sheet for each pair; A3 enlargement of 'Division'; individual whiteboards and pens.

Further support
If possible, ask an adult to work with less able children. Ask the adult to use an A3 enlargement of the activity sheet, pinned to a flipchart. Children take it in turns to choose a number for which they know a division sentence, so that they have success at this. At the point where children start to struggle, suggest to the adult that the children consider which table the number belongs to. For example, if it is an odd number it cannot be a multiple of 2, 4 or 10. If it ends in 5 or 0 then it is in the 5 times-table, and so on. Then children can say together the table they chose to see if they find the number, and then derive a division fact to fit.

Oral and mental starter

Ask the children to draw this triangle on their whiteboards.

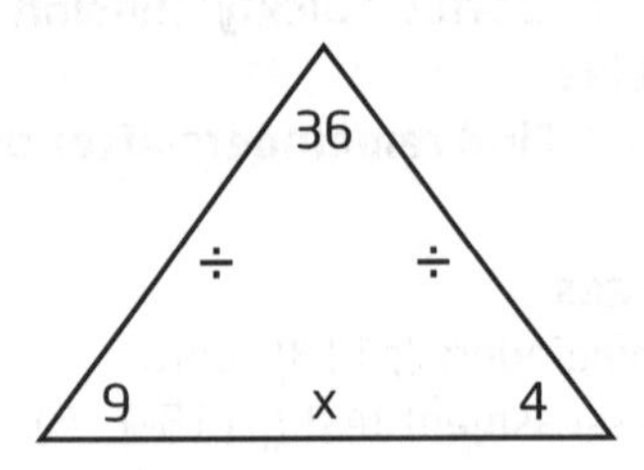

Ask them to think about numbers that would complete the number sentences, that is 9 and 4. Invite a child to say the sentences: 36 divided by 9 is 4; 36 divided by 4 is 9; 4 multiplied by 9 is 36. Repeat this with different numbers at the top of the triangle, chosen from the 2, 3, 4, 5 and 10 times-tables.

Main assessment activity

Pin the A3 enlargement of the 'Division' activity sheet to the board. Point to the number 24 and explain that this is the number that begins a division sentence in the 2, 3, 4, 5 or 10 times-table. Invite suggestions for what the answer could be. Children may suggest $24 \div 3 = 8$ or $24 \div 4 = 6$. Repeat this for another number from the grid, such as 16.

Ask the children to work in pairs, with a copy of the activity sheet between them. They must decide who will write a tick and who a cross. One child then chooses a number from the grid. Their partner says a division sentence that begins with the chosen number, in the form: *x divided by y is z*. If they agree that this is correct, the child who said the number sentence writes their mark (tick or cross) over the chosen number. They repeat this, taking it in turns to choose a number, until all the numbers in the grid have been ticked or crossed. The children count the number of ticks or crosses to see who has won the game.

Observe the children you are targeting for assessment. Listen in to their responses and check that they are able to derive the answer rapidly. Ask probing questions, such as:
- *Which multiplication fact uses the same numbers?*
- *Can you think of another division fact that uses these numbers?*

Plenary

Using the A3 enlargement of the activity sheet again, divide the class into two teams, each with a team captain. One team can be tick and the other cross. Play the game again, this time with the team captains choosing the number for the opposing team. Each child can only be chosen once, and the game is over when everyone in the team has had a turn. Ask probing questions, such as: *How many division facts can you make with the number 20? ...16? ... 36?*

Division

- Work with a partner.
  - One of you will use ✔ the other ✘.
  - The numbers in the grid are all start numbers for divisions by 2, 3, 4, 5 or 10.
  - Take turns to choose a number from the grid.
  - Ask your partner to say a division sentence that starts with your chosen number.
  - If you agree, your partner can put their mark (tick or cross) over that number.
  - When all the numbers have been marked, count up the ticks and the crosses.
  - The winner is the player who has more questions correct.

2	45	80	32	24	12	15	16	10	30
36	27	90	12	60	18	25	24	6	30
30	8	40	16	20	10	28	8	3	5
40	10	15	20	21	20	35	40	4	50
18	20	4	12	50	15	70	6	9	100

Remainders

Key objective:
Find remainders after division.

What you need
- A copy of the 'Remainders' activity sheet for each child; A3 enlargement of 'Remainders'; two sets of 0-9 numeral cards for each pair of children.

Further support
Ask an adult to work with less able children. Decide whether to limit the children to TU numbers to 60 by providing two piles of numeral cards for each pair: 1-2 in the tens pile, and 0-9 in the units pile for dividing by 2; then the tens pile can have 1-3 for dividing by 3; 1-4 for dividing by 4; 1-5 for dividing by 5 and 1-9 for dividing by 10. The children should concentrate on dividing by 2 five times, by 3 five times, and so on.

Oral and mental starter
Explain that you will ask a division question that has a remainder. Ask the children to write the remainder on their whiteboards and to hold up their boards when you say 'Show me'. Ask, for instance: *What is the remainder when I divide 15 by 2? ... 18 by 5? ... 20 by 3? ... 36 by 10?*

Main assessment activity
Pin up the A3 enlargement of the 'Remainders' activity sheet. Invite a child to take the top two cards from a shuffled set of 0-9 numeral cards. Show the other children the cards and make a TU number with them. Now choose a number from the spinner which, when divided into the TU number, will give a remainder. Invite the children to say the division sentence, including the remainder.

Explain that the children will work in pairs to play this as a game, taking turns to choose two cards and to make a TU number. They spin the paperclip with their pencil and where the clip stops on the spinner gives them their divider. If the children cannot work mentally to solve a division, explain that they can use the back of their sheet to make jottings.

Observe the children you are targeting for assessment. Check that they use their table facts to help them to divide, and that they divide accurately. Ask them probing questions, such as: *Tell me some divisions that leave a remainder of 1 ... 2 ... 3 ... 4* and so on.

Plenary
Invite the children whom you are targeting for assessment to say one of their division sentences, without the answer. Ask the other children to calculate the answer and for the child whose division sentence it is to state whether they think the answer is correct or not, and why they think this.

Ask probing questions such as:
- *Do all division sentences have remainders?*
- *Make up a division sentence with a remainder of 1... 2 ... 3 ... 4.*
- *How did you do this?*
- *Make up some division sentences with no remainders.*
- *How did you do this? Why do these not have a remainder?*

Name Date

Remainders

- Work with a partner.
- ☐ You will need two sets of 0–9 numeral cards and a paper clip.
- ☐ Shuffle the numeral cards.
- ☐ Take turns to take two cards and make a TU number.
- ☐ Spin the paperclip on the spinner.
- ☐ Divide the card number by the spinner number.
- ☐ Write the division sentence, the answer and any remainder.
- ☐ Repeat this until you have written 20 division sentences.

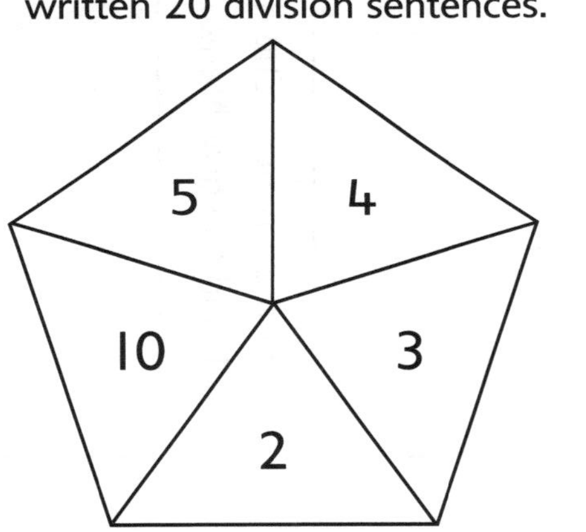

1 ☐ ÷ ☐ = ______

2 ☐ ÷ ☐ = ______

3 ☐ ÷ ☐ = ______

4 ☐ ÷ ☐ = ______

5 ☐ ÷ ☐ = ______

6 ☐ ÷ ☐ = ______

7 ☐ ÷ ☐ = ______

8 ☐ ÷ ☐ = ______

9 ☐ ÷ ☐ = ______

10 ☐ ÷ ☐ = ______

11 ☐ ÷ ☐ = ______

12 ☐ ÷ ☐ = ______

13 ☐ ÷ ☐ = ______

14 ☐ ÷ ☐ = ______

15 ☐ ÷ ☐ = ______

16 ☐ ÷ ☐ = ______

17 ☐ ÷ ☐ = ______

18 ☐ ÷ ☐ = ______

19 ☐ ÷ ☐ = ______

20 ☐ ÷ ☐ = ______

Name Date

Word problems

- Write the answers to these word problems.
  - Write your jottings.

Michelle thinks that $\frac{2}{6}$ of her stickers are blue. Mandy told Michelle that another way of saying this was that $\frac{1}{3}$ of her stickers are blue. Do you agree with Mandy? Explain why.

Chu Hua wanted to share some sweets with her friends. There were three friends and Chu Hua. There were 38 sweets. How many sweets could each have? How many are left over?

Laurie counted out 15 red marbles and 18 blue marbles. He decided to put the marbles into a bag and mix them up. Then he shared the marbles between Ubora, Duman, Kerem and himself. How many marbles did they have each? How many marbles were left over?

Leila had 24 pencils. She decided to give $\frac{2}{6}$ of her pencils to Neylan. How many pencils did she give Neylan? What fraction did she have left for herself?

Name Date

Assessment 4

1. Write the answers to these division sentences.

1	4	÷	2	=									
6	0	÷	1	0	=								
2	4	÷	4	=									
3	5	÷	5	=									
3	6	÷	4	=									
8	0	÷	1	0	=								
1	5	÷	3	=									
4	5	÷	5	=									
1	8	÷	2	=									
2	7	÷	3	=									

2. Some of these division sentences have remainders.

- ▢ Decide how to work out the answers.
- ▢ Show your jottings.

1	6	÷	3	=									
3	8	÷	2	=									
5	6	÷	5	=									
5	0	÷	4	=									

Name Date

3. Write the missing fractions in these number sentences.

$\frac{1}{2} + \frac{1}{4} + \frac{\square}{\square} = 1$

$\frac{6}{8} = \frac{\square}{4}$

$\frac{1}{3} + \frac{2}{6} = \frac{\square}{\square}$

$\frac{1}{5} + \frac{2}{10} + \frac{\square}{\square} = 1$

4. Write the answers to these word problems.

Josh bought 50 sweets to share with his four friends. How many did they each have? Were there any left over?

____

____

Ashley and Hannah wanted to buy four books. Each book cost £4. They had £20 to spend. How much did they spend? How much change did they receive?

____

____

Michael had £30 to spend. He wanted to buy some CDs. Each CD cost £4. How many CDs could he buy? How much change would he have?

____

____

Alexis had 83 swap cards to share with her brother Brandon. How many swap cards did they each have? How many were there left over?

____

____

Assess and Review

Key objectives to be assessed

Assessment lesson 1: **Round any positive integer less than 1000 to the nearest 10 or 100.**
Assessment lesson 2: **Use symbols correctly, including less than (<), greater than (>), equals (=).**

Photocopiable pages
Four in a line (p119); Greater and smaller (p121); Numbers, measures and shapes (p122); Assessment test (p123-124).

Equipment
Individual whiteboards and pens; red and blue pencils; counters; 0-9 numeral cards; paper; stopwatch or clock.

Assessment Activities

Mental maths assessment

Round any positive integer less than 1000 to the nearest 10 or 100 b

Ask the children to round numbers to the nearest 10 or 100. They can write their answers on their whiteboards and when you say 'Show me', hold up their boards for you to see. Say, for example: *Round these numbers to the nearest 10: 64, 92, 156, 209, 551.* Repeat this for rounding to the nearest 100, using numbers such as 356, 549, 888.

Probing questions

- *I rounded a number to the nearest 10. My answer is 540. What could my starting number have been?*
- *I rounded a number to the nearest 100. My answer is 300. What could my starting number have been?*

Written maths assessment

Provide each child with a copy of the 'Numbers, measures and shapes' activity sheet and check that they understand what to do for each part of the sheet. You can ask all the children in the class to complete this sheet and then ask small, targeted groups of children, whose progress you are unsure about, the probing questions listed below.

Probing questions

1. Use symbols correctly, including less than (<), greater than (>), equals (=) a

- *What symbols would you use to make this true: 50 □ 30 □ 40?*
- *What numbers could you put into this number sentence to make it true: □ > □?*

2. Carry out column subtraction of two integers less than 1000 e

- *What tips would you give to someone learning to do column subtraction?*

3. Know and use the relationships between familiar units of length, mass and capacity i

- *Tell me another way to write 4km ...600g ...1.5l.*

4. Classify polygons, using criteria such as number of right angles, whether or not they are regular, symmetry properties j

- *Tell me a polygon which fits the criteria 'has all sides the same length and two lines of symmetry'.*

Four in a line

Key objective:
Round any positive integer less than 1000 to the nearest 10 or 100.

What you need
- A copy of the 'Four in a line' activity sheet for each pair; A3 enlargement of 'Four in a line'; red and blue pencils and a counter for each pair; two sets of 0-9 numeral cards for each pair.

Further support
Decide whether to limit the less able children to rounding to the nearest 10. When they are confident at this, they can play the game rounding only to the nearest 100. When they are confident with both rounding to the nearest 10 and nearest 100, they can play the game as it is written.

Oral and mental starter

Say: *I have rounded a number to the nearest 10. My rounded number is 490. What could my starting number be?* Invite the children to take turns to suggest what the starting number could be (485 to 494) and write these on the board. Repeat this for another number rounded to the nearest 10. Then repeat for rounding to the nearest 100.

Main assessment activity

Pin the enlarged version of the 'Four in a line' activity sheet on the wall. Invite a child to choose three cards and to make a HTU number with these. Write the number on the board. Point to the circle on the sheet. Ask the children to round the HTU number to the nearest 10 and agree what this.

Now explain the activity to the children. Say: *Working in pairs, you will take turns to take three cards and make a HTU number. One of you will drop a counter onto the rounding circle. Now round your number to the nearest 10 or 100 and decide where to write it in the grid, using your coloured pencil. The object of the game is to get four numbers in a row in your colour.*

Show the children that the row could be horizontal, vertical or diagonal. Explain that as they take turns they need to make sure that they spot where their partner could make a row, and put their own number to block their partner. Remind the children that this game may be very like a commercial game that they play with friends. They should think of the same 'blocking' moves to stop their partner from winning.

The object of this game is to ensure that the children round numbers appropriately to the nearest 10 or 100, so as they play, check that those for whom you need more assessment information are making appropriate rounding decisions.

Plenary

Divide the class into two teams, each with a captain. The captains take turns to make a three-digit number from the cards. The opposing captain decides whether to ask for a number rounded to 10 or 100. The first captain chooses a team member to say the rounded number. The captain writes the number into a grid space on the enlarged sheet.

Play the game until one of the teams has won. Then ask some probing questions about rounding, such as:

- *The newspaper wrote that 700 people attended a play in the park. This was given to the nearest 100. What is the smallest number that attended? What is the largest number that attended?*
- *How would you explain to someone how to round to the nearest 10? ...100?*

Four in a line

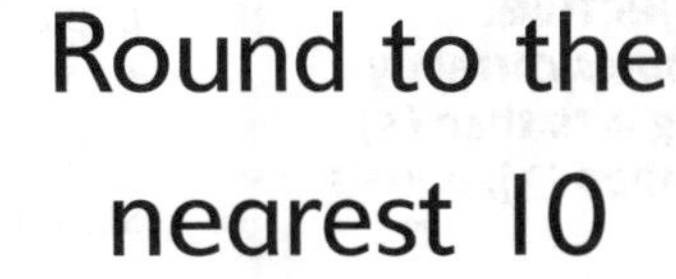

- Play this game with a friend.
- You will need a counter, a red pencil for one of you and a blue pencil for the other, and two sets of shuffled 0–9 cards.
  - ☐ Take turns to take the top three cards and make a HTU number.
  - ☐ Take turns to drop a counter onto the spinner.
  - ☐ This tells you whether to round the number to the nearest 10 or 100.
  - ☐ Decide where to write your number in the grid. Use your coloured pencil.
  - ☐ The first person to get four numbers in a line wins the game.
  - ☐ The line can be horizontal, vertical or diagonal.

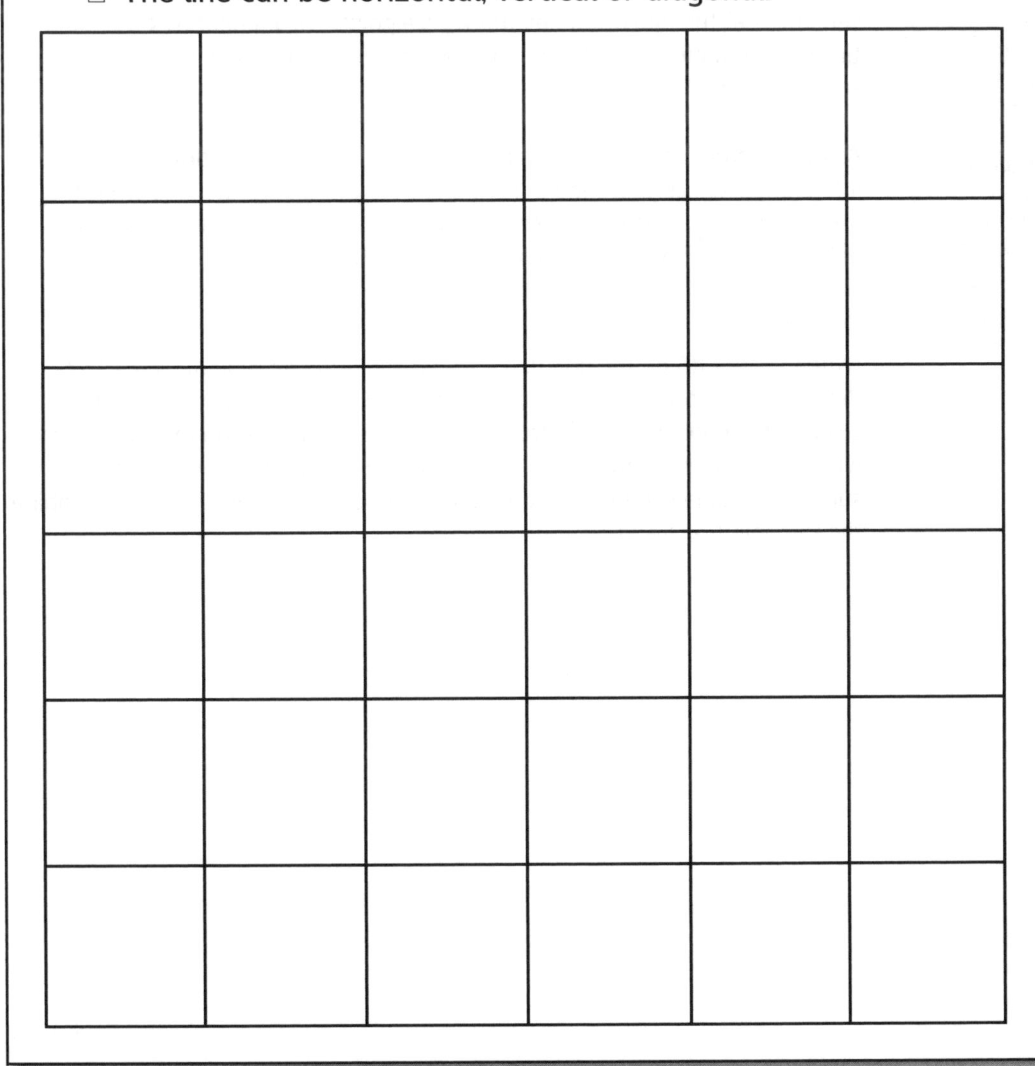

Greater and smaller

Key objective:
Use symbols correctly, including less than (<), greater than (>), equals (=).

What you need
- A copy of the 'Greater and smaller' activity sheet for each pair; A3 enlargement of 'Greater and smaller'; a stopwatch or clock (or a classroom clock with a second hand); two sets of 0-9 numeral cards for each pair; individual whiteboards and pens; paper for each child.

Further support
Decide whether to limit less able children to choosing just three cards each time to make pairs of HTU numbers to fit the number sentence □ > □, then □ < □. They can play the game in the same way as the rest of the class.

Oral and mental starter

Explain that you will show the children four numeral cards. Ask them to make two numbers from these cards and write them on their whiteboards. The numbers must fit the number sentence □ > □. Repeat this for the number sentence □ < □.

Main assessment activity

Pin up the enlarged version of the 'Greater and smaller' activity sheet and explain how to play the game. Begin by inviting a child to choose four numeral cards to make a ThHTU number. Using the same numbers, invite a child to make another number with the same cards. Write the number sentence □ > □ on the board and invite a child to write in the two numbers made to make the sentence true. Now invite all the children to write two more numbers on their whiteboards using the same digits. They write their numbers into the number sentence □ > □. Repeat this for the number sentence □ < □.

Now explain that you would like the children to work in pairs to play a game. They take turns to choose four numeral cards and use the digits to make two ThHTU that fit the number sentence □ > □. Explain that they have one minute to do this and must time themselves. Whoever has more correct number sentences at the end of the minute wins a point. They repeat this four more times. Then they repeat it another five times, this time using the number sentence □ < □.

As the children work, observe those for whom you are collecting assessment information. Check that they understand the symbols < and > and what they mean in number sentences. Ask these children to place the correct symbol between pairs of numbers, such as 4567 and 9781.

Plenary

Write □ + ◊ = 25 on the board. Ask: *What could the missing numbers be?* Repeat this for other number sentences using +, – and =, encouraging the children for whom you are gathering assessment information to answer. Now write this number sentence on the board: □ + ◊ < 50. Ask the children to suggest possible solutions. Repeat for other number sentences which combine the symbols +, –, < and >.

Name Date

Greater and smaller

- Work with a partner. You will need two sets of shuffled 0–9 numeral cards and a clock or watch.
  - Take turns to choose four cards. You can now make lots of ThHTU numbers with these four digits.
  - Both of you use the four cards to make as many number sentences as you can in one minute to fit the number sentence ☐ > ☐.
  - Write the number sentences on some paper.
  - Whoever has more number sentences that you both agree are correct wins a point.
  - Do this again four more times.
  - Now do this again five more times, using the number sentence ☐ < ☐.

Name	Points	Name	Points
Total		Total	

Who won? ____________________

Name Date

Numbers, measures and shapes

- Use the symbols < , > or = to make these number sentences true.

569 ☐ 497

361 ☐ 479

555 ☐ 500 + 50

13 + 266 ☐ 279

- Use the column subtraction method that your teacher showed you.
  - ☐ Work out the answers to these subtraction questions:

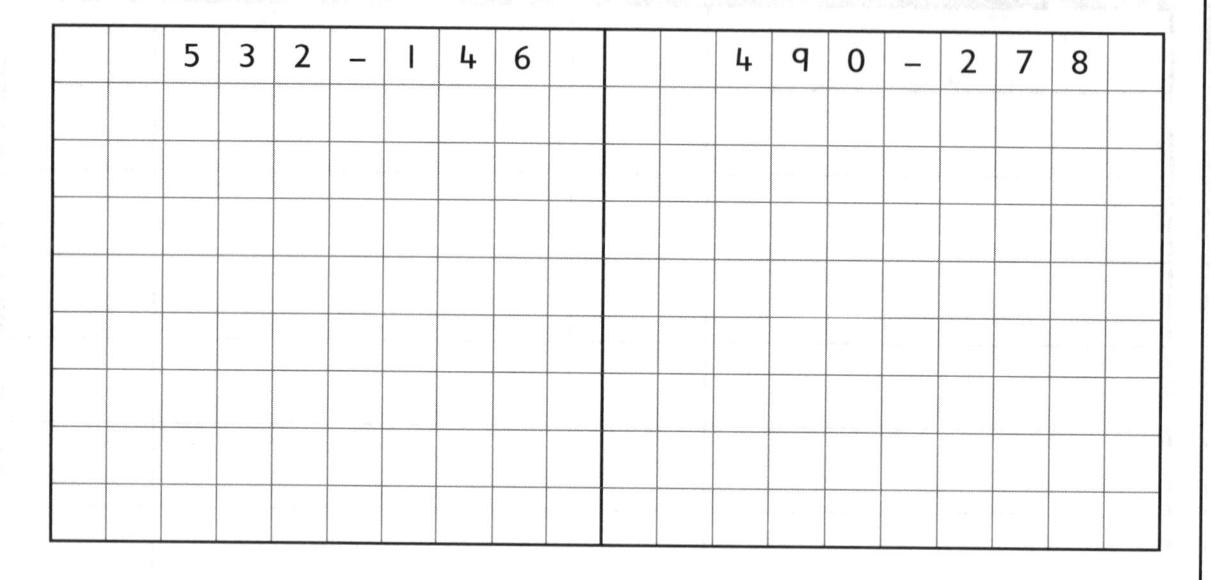

- Write these measurements in their new units.

500g = ☐ kg 16mm = ☐ cm 0.65l = ☐ ml

- On the back of this sheet, sketch these two shapes, and write their names:
  - ☐ This shape has all its sides the same length and four lines of symmetry.
  - ☐ This shape has three sides the same length. All its angles are equal.

Name Date

Assessment 5

1. These numbers have been rounded to the nearest 10.

- Write three numbers that the starting number might be.

870 ________ ________ ________

5990 ________ ________ ________

2. These numbers have been rounded to the nearest 100.

- Write three numbers that the starting number might be.

4700 ________ ________ ________

5000 ________ ________ ________

3. Write the numbers 2567, 2675 and 2765 into this number sentence.

________ < ________ > ________

4. Now write a number to make this number sentence true.

45 + ________ < 25 + 30

5. Use the column subtraction method that your teacher has taught you to find the answers to these subtraction questions

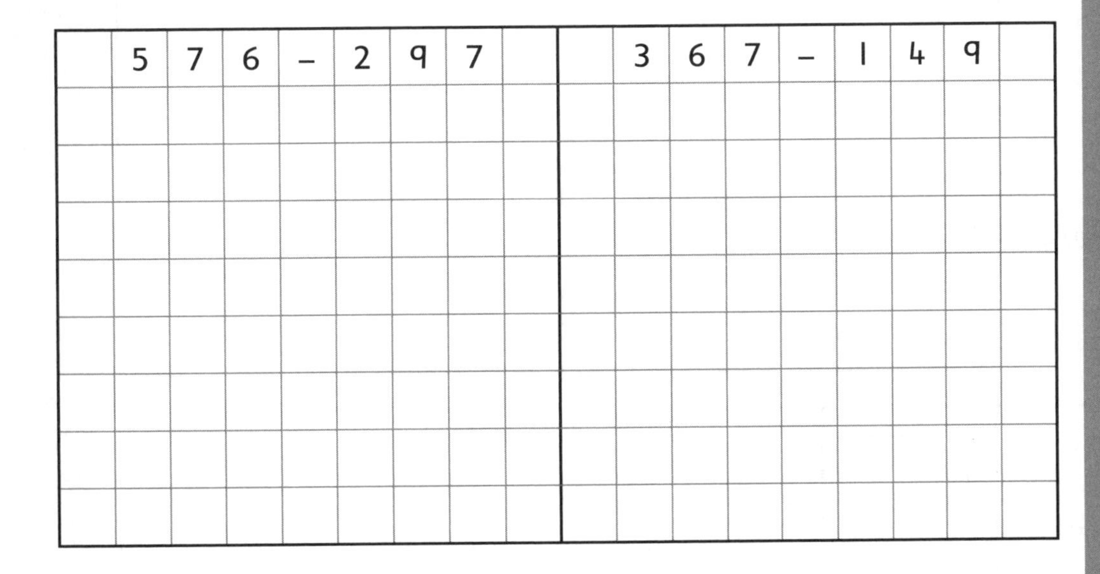

Name Date

6. Read these scales. Write the amount for each.

______ metres

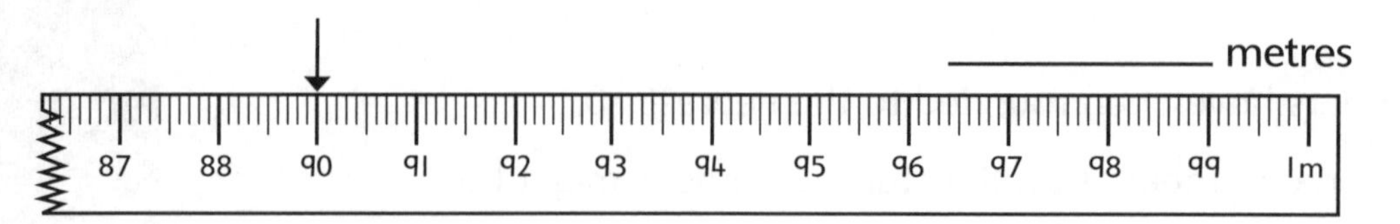

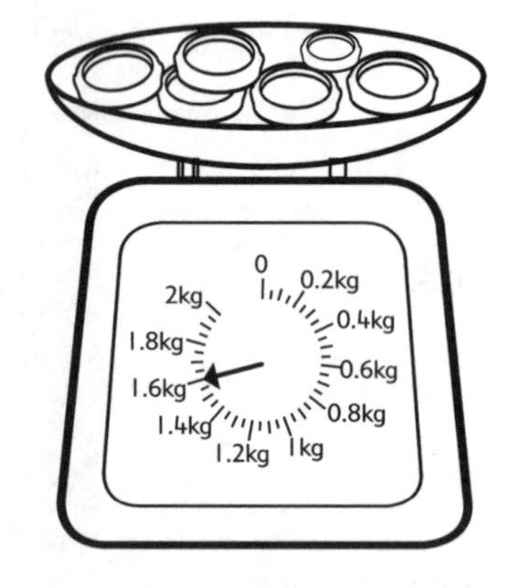

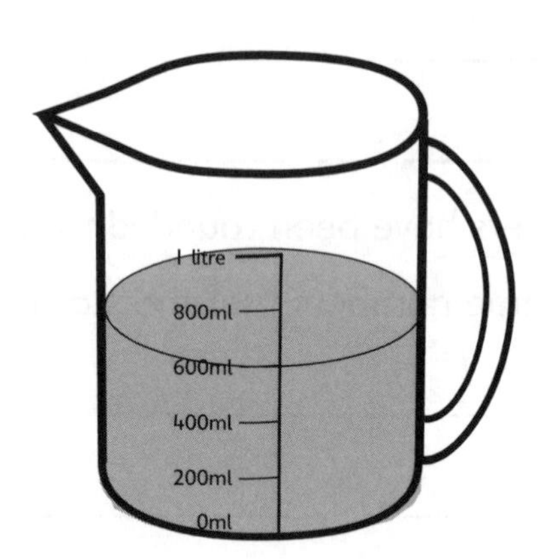

______ grams ______ litres

7. Cut out the shapes at the bottom of this page. Sort them onto this Carroll diagram.

	Triangles	Not triangles
Regular		
Irregular		

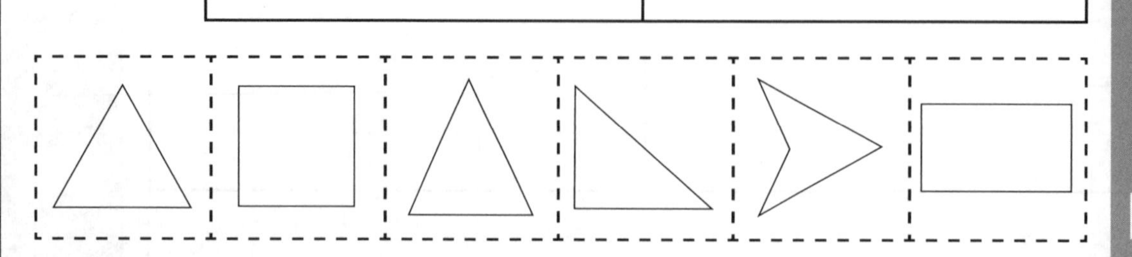

Assess and Review

Key objectives to be assessed

Assessment lesson 1: **Use known number facts and place value to subtract mentally, including any pair of two-digit whole numbers.**

Assessment lesson 2: **Use known number facts and place value to add mentally, including any pair of two-digit whole numbers.**

Photocopiable pages

Find the difference (p127); Mental addition (p129); Number quiz (p130); Assessment test (p131-132).

Equipment

Individual whiteboards and pens; red and blue counters; scissors.

Assessment Activities

Mental maths assessment

Use known number facts and place value to add or subtract mentally, including any pair of two-digit whole numbers d

Explain that all the questions you will ask will be about the number 100. Invite the children to write their answers on their whiteboards, and when you say 'Show me', they hold these up for you to see. Say, for example: *What must I add to 37 to make 100? What is 45 add 55? How much must I add to 17 to make 100?*

Probing questions

- *How did you work this out?*
- *Is there another method you could use?*
- *How could you check your answer?*

Written maths assessment

Provide each child with a copy of the 'Number quiz' activity sheet. You can ask the whole class to complete this sheet. If you do this you can then ask the probing questions of small, targeted groups of children whose progress against the key objectives you are unsure of. Alternatively, you can work with a targeted group and use the probing questions as the children work.

Probing questions

1. Derive quickly division facts corresponding to the 2, 3, 4, 5 and 10 multiplication tables g

- *How many multiplication and division facts can you make using what you know about 24?*
- *How did you work out the division facts?*

2. Choose and use appropriate number operations and ways of calculating (mental, mental with jottings, pencil and paper) to solve problems k

- *How did you know whether to add, subtract, multiply or divide?*

3. Recognise simple fractions that are several parts of a whole, and mixed numbers; recognise the equivalence of simple fractions c

- *Tell me some fractions that are greater than ½. How do you know?*

4. Carry out column addition and subtraction of two integers less than 1000, and column addition of more than two such integers e

- *What tips would you give to someone to help them with column addition?*

Find the difference

Key objective:
Use known number facts and place value to subtract mentally, including any pair of two-digit whole numbers.

What you need
- A copy of the 'Find the difference' activity sheet for each pair; A3 enlargement of 'Find the difference'; 15 red and 15 blue counters for each pair.

Further support
Ask an adult to work with the less able children, as a group. Pin an A3 enlargement of 'Find the difference' to a flipchart. Ask the adult to choose two numbers from the scroll for the children to find the difference between them. Then, ask the children to explain how they worked out the answer. Discuss the different methods and which one the children think is better, and why. Where children are unsure, ask the adult to model the mental method that is best for the particular problem, then to give a further example for the children to try for themselves.

Oral and mental starter

Explain that you will ask the children some subtraction questions. Ask them to put up their hands to answer. Say, for example: *What is the difference between 130 and 60? How many must I subtract from 800 to leave 500? What is 86 subtract 40? What is 530 subtract 290? How much must I subtract from 743 to leave 443? What is the difference between 8000 and 6? What is 4973 subtract 8? What is the difference between 84 and 37?* Ask other similar subtraction questions.

Main assessment activity

Pin up the A3 enlargement of the 'Find the difference' activity sheet. Explain the task to the children and ask them to work in pairs. Each child will need about 15 counters. Say: *Take turns to choose two numbers from the scroll. Find the difference between them. Check that your partner agrees with your answer. If your answer is on the treasure chest, cover it with a counter. The winner is the player with more counters on the chest when all the numbers are covered.* Check that everybody understands what to do and ask the children to begin.

As the children work, target those for whom you need further assessment information. Ask questions such as: *How did you work that out? Is there another way? Which way is better? Why do you think that?*

Plenary

Choose two scroll numbers from the 'Find the difference' sheet and invite the children to explain how they found the answer. Target children for whom you are collecting assessment evidence to answer. Repeat this for other pairs of numbers. Ask probing questions, such as:

- *What method did you use to work out the answer to this calculation?*
- *Who used a different method?*
- *Which method do you think is better? Why do you think that?*
- *How could you check that your answer is correct?*

Discuss any mental methods that the children found difficult. Give further examples and ask the children to practise that method.

Find the difference

- Work with a partner.
  - You each need about 15 counters.
  - Take turns to choose two numbers from the scroll.
  - Find the difference between them.
  - Check that your partner agrees with your answer.
  - If your answer is on the treasure chest, cover it with a counter.
- The winner is the player with more counters on the chest when all the numbers are covered.

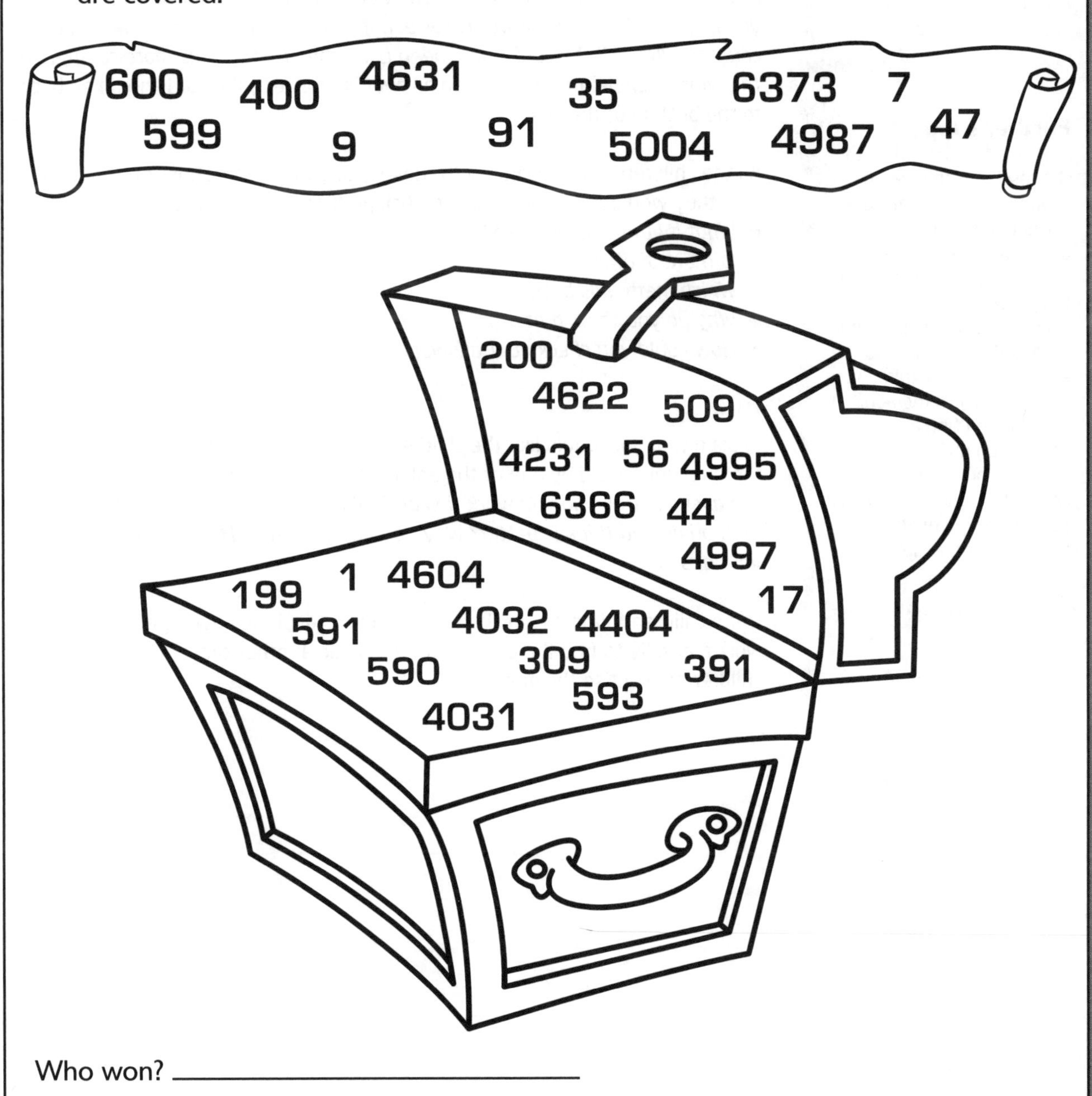

Who won? ____________________

Mental addition

Key objective:
Use known number facts and place value to add mentally, including any pair of two-digit whole numbers.

What you need
- A copy of the 'Mental addition' activity sheet for each child; A3 enlargement of 'Mental addition' with the cards cut out; scissors; 20 counters for each pair of children.

Further support
Ask an adult to work with the less able children in a group. Each child can take turns to answer the question on a card, and if their answer is correct then they can have a counter. However, every child should work out the answer to each card, then explain how they did this to the adult. If the children find a calculation difficult, ask the adult to show how to calculate it and then to give further examples for the children to practise the method.

Oral and mental starter

Explain that you will ask the children some addition questions. Ask them to put up their hands to answer. Say, for example: *What is 30 add 80? What must I add to 700 to get a total of 1200? What is 90 add 17? ... 300 add 275? ... 5000 add 617? What must be added to 45 to make 100? What do I need to add to 562 to make 600? What must be added to 8500 to make 9000? What is the total of 537 and 8? What is 5846 add 7? What is 54 add 29?* Ask other similar addition questions.

Main assessment activity

Explain to the children that they will be playing a game in pairs. Ask the pairs to quickly cut out one set of addition cards from the 'Mental addition' activity sheet. Say: *Shuffle the cards and place them in a stack face down on the table. Now take turns to take a card and work out the answer. Your partner will tell you if they think your answer is correct. If the answer is correct, then take a counter. When all the cards have been used the one who has more counters is the winner.* Explain that where an answer is incorrect, the card should go back to the bottom of the pile.

As the children work, discuss with those that you are targeting for assessment how they worked out their answers. Ask probing questions, such as:

- *What method did you use?*
- *Is there another way?*
- *Which method is better?*
- *Why do you think that?*
- *How could you check your answer?*

Plenary

Explain that you would like the children to explain how they worked out each of the questions. Hold up one of the enlarged cards for all to see and ask: *What is the answer? How did you work this out? Who used a different method? Which method do you think is better? Why do you think that? How could you check your answer?*

If the children found any of the calculations difficult, review together how to work mentally to find the answer, then provide another similar question for the children to practise the method.

Name Date

Mental addition

- Work with a partner.
  - You will need 20 counters.
  - Cut out the cards and shuffle them.
  - Take turns to take a card.
  - Read the question and say the answer.
  - If your partner agrees, take a counter.
- The player with more counters when all the cards have been used is the winner.

50 + 80	What should I add to 90 to make 140?	What should I add to 47 to make 100?	What must I add to 278 to make 285?
300 + 800	260 + 17	What should I add to 536 to make 600?	What must I add to 5279 to make 5285?
63 add 30	750 + 38	What should I add to 4600 to make 5000?	54 + 28
90 + 19	3000 + 429	539 + 4	What must I add to 27 to get 56?
What should I add to 23 to make 100?	300 + 456	2498 + 5	What must I add to 45 to get 72?

Name Date

Number quiz

- Write the answers to these number problems.
  - Show your jottings.

Damien has four brothers. They all decide to share 45 marbles. How many do they get each?
Nancy has 27p. How many mint balls at 3p each can she buy?
Gareth counted his model cars. He has 256. His brother has 157. Use a column addition method to find out how many cars Gareth and his brother have altogether.

- Shade in the fractions shown for each of these.

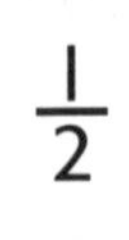
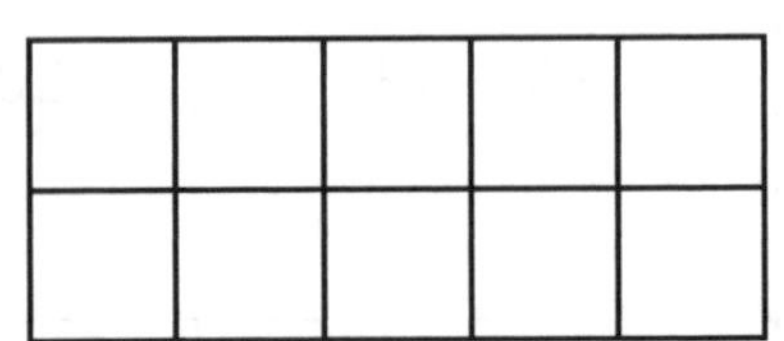

$\frac{2}{3}$ 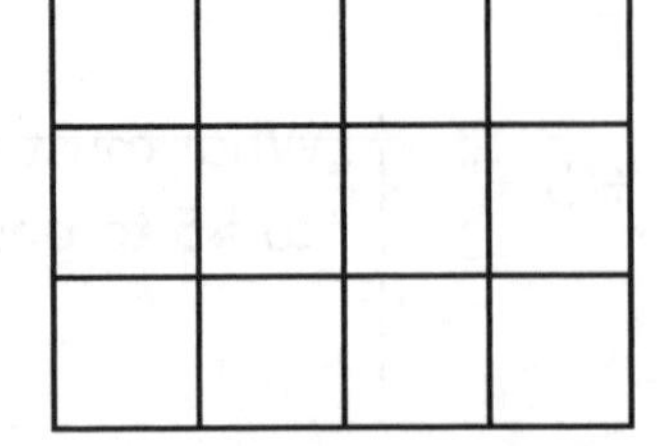

$\frac{5}{8}$ 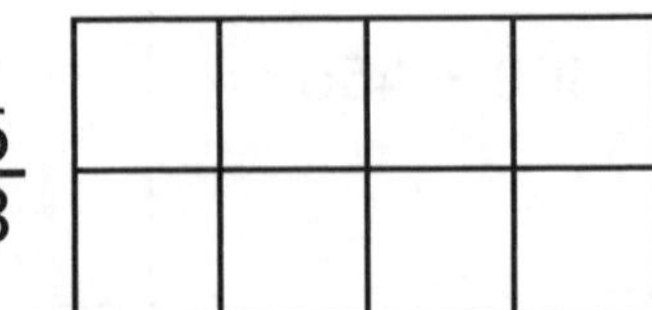

$\frac{2}{3}$ 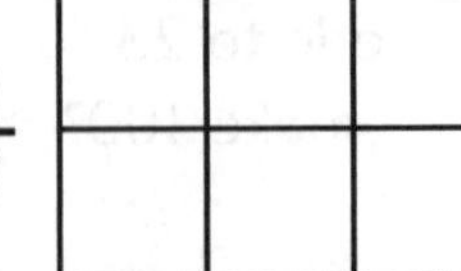

Name Date

Assessment 6

1. Write the answers to these addition and subtraction questions.

37	+	☐	=	100	527	+	6	=	☐
100	–	☐	=	58	6327	+	8	=	☐
300	+	900	=	☐	800	–	8	=	☐
64	+	20	=	☐	5000	–	4	=	☐
561	+	30	=	☐	5362	–	7	=	☐
90	+	16	=	☐	8002	–	7989	=	☐
450	+	18	=	☐	5005	–	4988	=	☐
5000	+	234	=	☐	53	+	27	=	☐
8200	+	☐	=	9000	53	–	27	=	☐

2. Write the answers to these division questions.

40	÷	5	=	☐	18	÷	3	=	☐
30	÷	10	=	☐	18	÷	2	=	☐
24	÷	4	=	☐	32	÷	4	=	☐

3. Write what fraction is shaded.

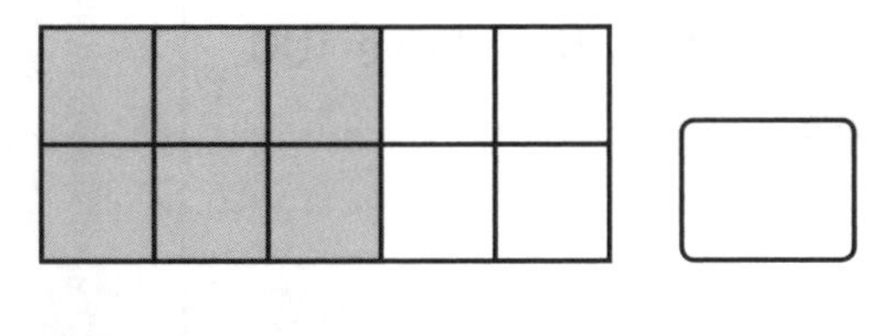

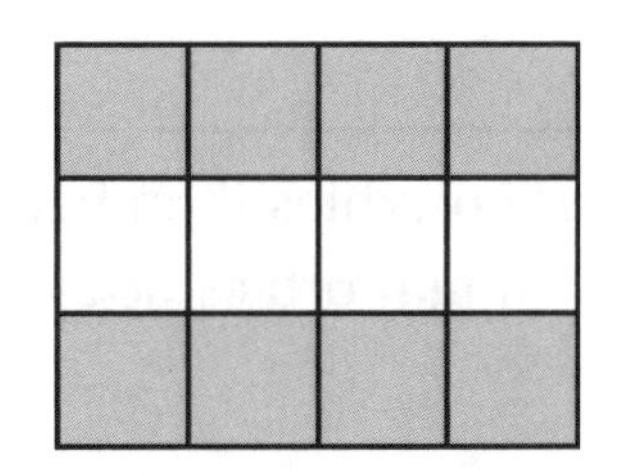

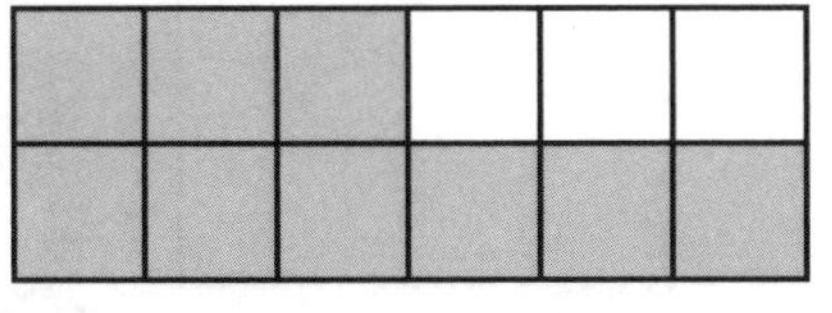

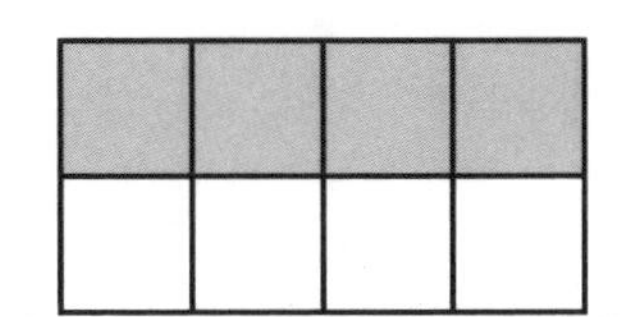

Name Date

4. Solve these addition questions.

- ▢ Use the column addition method that your teacher has shown you.

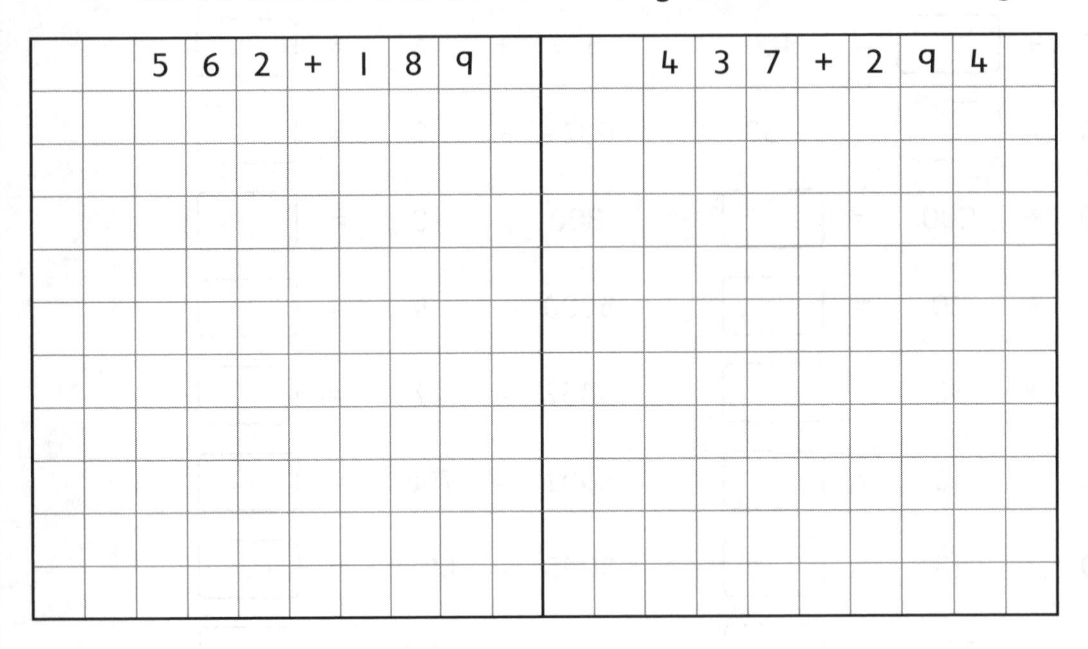

5. Write the answers to these problems.

- ▢ Show your jottings.

Marcus has 335 marbles and his brother has 468 marbles. How many marbles do they have altogether?

Julia has 16 more marbles than her sister. Altogether they have 100 marbles. How many marbles does Julia have?

End-of-year assessment

There are two forms of end-of-year assessment:

- Mental tests: there are two of these. Each has its own photocopiable sheet on which the children write their answers.
- Check-ups: these are written tests covering all the key objectives for the year.

The test questions are matched to the key objectives in the table below. Where you are still unsure whether a child has achieved a key objective, use the probing questions in the table for the relevant key objective to help you to make an informed decision about achievement.

Key objective	Written test question number	Probing questions
a	1	Which numbers could you choose to make this correct: ▢ < ▢ ?
b	2	I rounded a number to the nearest 10. The answer is 260. What could my starting number be?
c	3	Which fractions are equivalent to $\frac{1}{2}$ ... $\frac{1}{4}$ ...?
d	4	How could you work out the answer? Could you use a different method? How could you check your answer?
e	5	Tell me some tips for doing column addition/ subtraction.
f	6	The product is 24. What two numbers could have been multiplied together?
g	7	Start with the number 36. How many different multiplication and division facts can you tell me?
h	8	Tell me a division which will have a remainder of 1. How did you work this out?
i	9	Tell me another way to write 2 litres, 300 grams, 45 centimetres...
j	10	Tell me the name of a regular polygon.
k	11	How do you know whether to add, subtract, multiply or divide? What word clues do you look for?

Mental maths test 1

Instructions

Explain to the children that you will read each question twice.
Ask them to write their name and the date at the top of their answer sheet.
For questions 1 to 10, allow 5 seconds before moving on to the next question.
For questions 11 to 16, allow 10 seconds.

Test 1

1. Write in numerals the number seven thousand and fifty six.
2. Put in a greater than or less than symbol to make the number sentence on your sheet true.
3. Round 491 to the nearest 10.
4. Round 537 to the nearest hundred.
5. Write the fraction two quarters in another way.
6. What is the total of 63 and 30?
7. What is 49 add 25?
8. What is the difference between 5007 and 4998?
9. What is 9 multiplied by 4?
10. What is 35 divided by 5?
11. What is the remainder when I divided 38 by 4?
12. How many grams are there in 1.4 kilograms?
13. Look at the two shapes on your sheet. Tick the one with two lines of symmetry.
14. Azar bought four oranges. Each orange cost 30p. How much change did she get from £5?
15. Salman saved up to buy a CD which cost £5.89. How much change did he get from £10?
16. Leonie went to the cinema to buy some tickets. Each ticket cost £3.50. How many tickets could she buy with £20?

Name Date

Mental maths test 1 recording sheet

- Listen to the questions, then write your answers in the spaces provided.

1.	
2.	564 ☐ 546
3.	
4.	
5.	
6.	
7.	
8.	
9.	
10.	
11.	
12.	
13.	
14.	
15.	
16.	

Mental maths test 2

Instructions

Explain to the children that you will read each question twice.
Ask them to write their name and the date at the top of their answer sheet.
For questions 1 to 10, allow 5 seconds before moving on to the next question.
For questions 11 to 16, allow 10 seconds.

Test 2

1. Write the number four thousand six hundred and six in numerals.
2. Use the greater or less than symbol to make the number sentence on your sheet true.
3. Round 449 to the nearest 10.
4. Round 449 to the nearest 100.
5. What is 900 subtract 7?
6. What is the total of 35 and 49?
7. What is the product of 6 and 3?
8. What is 9 multiplied by 2?
9. How many tens are there in thirty?
10. What is 40 divided by 5?
11. What is the remainder when I divide 48 by 5?
12. Write the remainder after dividing 29 by 3.
13. How many centimetres are there in 4.2 metres?
14. Write the name of the triangle with three sides the same length.
15. Donata had £25 to spend. She bought three books at £8 each. How much change did she receive?
16. The cake went in the oven at 2.20. It cooked for fifty minutes. What time did it come out of the oven?

Name Date

Mental maths test 2 recording sheet

- Listen to the questions, then write your answers in the spaces provided.

1.	
2.	6549 ☐ 6594
3.	
4.	
5.	
6.	
7.	
8.	
9.	
10.	
11.	
12.	
13.	
14.	
15.	
16.	

Name ____ Date ____

Check-ups

1. Write in <, > or = to make these number sentences true.

450 ____ 380+70   8971 ____ 6493   2456 ____ 2546

2. Round these numbers to the nearest 10.

634 ____

595 ____

709 ____

Round these numbers to the nearest 100.

451 ____

609 ____

777 ____

3. Write the answers to these fraction sentences.

$\frac{1}{2} + \frac{2}{4} =$

$\frac{1}{6} + \frac{1}{6} + \frac{1}{3} + \frac{1}{3} =$

4. Write the answers to these addition and subtraction questions.

80 + 40 = ____

120 – 60 = ____

400 + 700 = ____

1300 – 800 = ____

56 + 40 = ____

86 – 40 = ____

530 + ____ = 563

4500 + ____ = 5000

1937 + 8 = ____

5000 – 7 = ____

506 – 7 = ____

5351 – 4 = ____

9007 – 8989 = ____

26 + 37 = ____

82 – 47 = ____

5. Set out these number sentences using the column addition or subtraction methods your teacher has taught you.

	5	6	4	+	2	7	8			5	7	3	–	1	8	6	

6. Write the answers to these multiplication sentences.

$6 \times 3 =$ ☐

$9 \times 2 =$ ☐

$10 \times 10 =$ ☐

$8 \times 3 =$ ☐

$6 \times 10 =$ ☐

$4 \times 5 =$ ☐

$4 \times 4 =$ ☐

$7 \times 5 =$ ☐

$8 \times 2 =$ ☐

$7 \times 4 =$ ☐

7. Write the answers to these division sentences.

$60 \div 10 =$ ☐

$32 \div 4 =$ ☐

$27 \div 3 =$ ☐

$30 \div 5 =$ ☐

$20 \div 2 =$ ☐

8. Write the answer to these division sentences. Write the remainder, too. Show your jottings.

$56 \div 5$

$49 \div 3$

Name Date

9. Write these measures in their new units.

Original units	New units
160cm	metres
$2\frac{1}{2}$ kilometres	metres
$3\frac{1}{4}$ kilograms	grams
750 grams	kilograms
650 ml	litres
$2\frac{3}{4}$ litres	ml

10. Sketch these two shapes.

a) It has four sides.
It has four right angles.
It has four lines of symmetry.

b) It has no sides the same length.
It has one right angle.
It has three sides.

11. Write the answers to these word problems.
Show your jottings.

a) There are five stacks of plates. Three stacks have 15 plates in them. Two stacks have 10 plates in them. How many plates altogether?

b) There are 36 children in the class. Half of them have cheese and onion crisps. A third of them have smoky bacon crisps. The rest do not have crisps. How many children do not have crisps?

Class record sheet

	Names																	
Key objectives: Year 4																		
Use symbols correctly, including less than (<), greater than (>), equals (=).																		
Round any positive integer less than 1000 to the nearest 10 or 100.																		
Recognise simple fractions that are several parts of a whole, and mixed numbers; recognise the equivalence of simple fractions.																		
Use known number facts and place value to add or subtract mentally, including any pair of two-digit whole numbers.																		
Carry out column addition and subtraction of two integers less than 1000, and column addition of more than two such integers.																		
Know by heart facts for the 2, 3, 4, 5 and 10 multiplication tables.																		
Derive quickly division facts corresponding to the 2, 3, 4, 5 and 10 multiplication tables.																		
Find remainders afer division.																		
Know and use the relationships between familiar units of length, mass and capacity.																		
Classify polygons, using criteria such as number of right angles, whether or not they are regular, symmetry properties.																		
Choose and use appropriate number operations and ways of calculating (mental, mental with jottings, pencil and paper) to solve problems.																		

Answer sheet

Autumn term

P89 **Word problems 1** 220. **2** 42. **3** 185.

P90 **Question allsorts** 589; 232, 432, 679.

P91 **Assessment test: autumn half-term 1**
1 centimetre, kilometre, millimetre, metre.
2 256, 495, 340, 522. **4** 24, 233.

P98 **What is missing?** 259, 897, 355, 329.
×, ÷, +, –.

P99 **Assessment test: autumn half-term 2**
1 $\frac{4}{8}$, $\frac{3}{10}$, $\frac{2}{8}$, $\frac{3}{6}$.
2 $\frac{1}{2}$, $\frac{1}{2}$, $\frac{2}{3}$, $\frac{3}{4}$ (these are suggestions only, there are other correct answers).
3 ÷, ×, –, +.
4 369, 563, 139, 478.

Spring term

P103 **Length and mass**
1000m, 100cm, 100mm, 1000g.
150 centimetres, 5000 grams, 6000 metres, $2\frac{1}{2}$ kilograms, 600 millimetres, $2\frac{1}{2}$ metres.
3 metres, 150g, 8mm, 7 metres.

P106 **Using numbers**
>, <, =, =.
560, 880, 420, 310.
900, 700, 700, 800.
11000g, 700cm.

P107 **Assessment test: spring half-term 1**
1 5 × 4 = 20, 4 × 5 = 20, 2 × 10 = 20, 10 × 2 = 20, 5 × 8 = 40, 8 × 5 = 40, 4 × 10 = 4, 10 × 4 = 40.
2 =, <, >, =.
3 m, kg, cm, g.
4 3 cakes and 50g left over; 3500g; $4\frac{3}{4}$ metres; 343km.

P114 **Word problems**
Yes, because $\frac{1}{3}$ is equivalent to $\frac{2}{6}$.
9 each and 2 left over 8 each and one left over.
Neylan received 8 pencils.
Leila had $\frac{2}{3}$ or $\frac{4}{6}$ left for herself.

P115 **Assessment test: spring half-term 2**
1 7, 6, 6, 7, 9, 8, 5, 9, 9, 9.
2 5 remainder 1; 19; 11 remainder 1; 12 remainder 2
3 $\frac{1}{4}$, $\frac{3}{4}$, $\frac{2}{3}$, $\frac{3}{5}$.
4 10, no remainder; £16 and £4 change; 7 CDs and £2 change; 41 each and 1 card remaining.

Summer term

P122 **Numbers, measures and shapes**
>, <, >, =.
386, 212.
0.5kg, 1.6cm, 650ml.
square, equilateral triangle.

P123 **Assessment test: summer half-term 1**
1 865 to 874, 5985 to 5994.
2 4650 to 4749, 4950 to 5449.
3 2567 < 2765 > 2675.
4 Any number between 0 and 9.
5 279, 218.
6 0.9 metres, 1600 grams, 0.6 litres.
7 See diagram below:

	Triangles	Not triangles
Regular	Equilateral triangle	square
Irregular	isosceles triangle right-angled triangle	arrow head rectangle

P127 **Find the difference**

Number	Number	Difference
600	400	200
599	600	1
599	400	199
600	9	591
400	9	391
599	9	590
4631	9	4622
4631	600	4031
4631	400	4231
4631	599	4032
91	35	56
600	91	509
400	91	309
5004	4987	17
5004	9	4995
5004	600	4404
5004	400	4604
6373	7	6366
5004	7	4997
600	7	593
47	91	44
35	47	12

Answer sheet

P129 Mental addition

Question card	Answer
50 + 80	130
What should I add to 90 to make 140?	50
300 + 800	1100
63 add 30	93
90 + 19	109
260 + 17	277
750 + 38	788
3000 + 429	3429
300 + 456	756
What should I add to 47 to make 100?	53
What should I add to 536 to make 600?	64
What should I add to 4600 to make 5000?	400
539 + 4	543
2498 + 5	2503
What must I add to 278 to make 285?	7
What must I add to 5279 to make 5285?	6
54 + 28	82
What must I add to 27 to get 56?	29
What must I add to 45 to get 72?	27
What should I add to 23 to make 100?	77

P130 Number quiz
9, 9, 413.

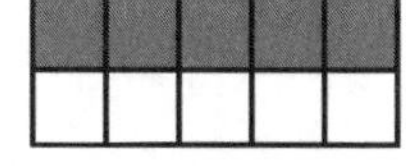

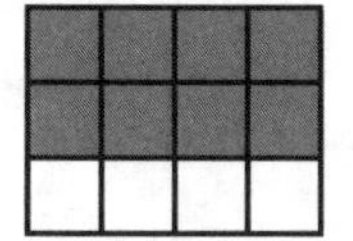

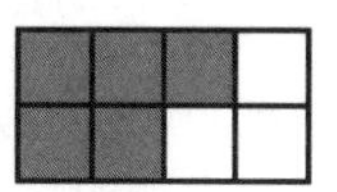

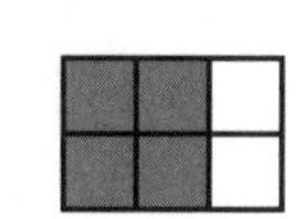

P131 Assessment test: summer half-term 2
1 63, 42, 1200, 84, 591, 106, 468, 5234, 800, 533, 6335, 792, 4996, 5355, 13, 17, 80, 26.
2 8, 3, 6, 6, 9, 8.
3 $\frac{6}{10}$ or $\frac{4}{5}$; $\frac{9}{12}$ or $\frac{3}{4}$; $\frac{8}{12}$ or $\frac{2}{3}$; $\frac{1}{2}$ or $\frac{4}{8}$.
4 751, 731.
5 803, 58.

End-of-year assessment

P134 Mental maths test 1
1 7056. **2** 564 > 546. **3** 490. **4** 500.
5 $\frac{1}{2}$. **6** 93. **7** 74. **8** 9. **9** 36. **10** 7. **11** 2.
12 1400 grams. **13** ✓ the first shape.
14 £3.80. **15** £4.11. **16** 5.

P136 Mental maths test 2
1 4606. **2** 6549 < 6594. **3** 450. **4** 400.
5 893. **6** 84. **7** 18. **8** 18. **9** 3. **10** 8.
11 3. **12**) 2. **13** 420 centimetres.
14 Equilateral. **15** £1. **16** 3.10.

P138 Check-ups
1 =, >, <.
2 nearest 10: 630, 600, 710;
nearest 100: 500, 600, 800.
3 1, 1.
4 120, 60, 1100, 500, 96, 46, 33, 500, 1945, 4993, 499, 5347, 18, 63, 35.
5 842, 387.
6 18, 20, 18, 16, 100, 35, 24, 16, 60, 28.
7 6, 6, 8, 10, 9.
8 11 remainder 1; 16 remainder 1.
9 1.6 metres, 2500 metres, 3250 grams, $\frac{3}{4}$kg or 0.75kg, 0.65 litres, 2750ml.
10 square, right-angled triangle
11 65, 6.

SCHOLASTIC

In this series:

ISBN 0-439-96512-8
ISBN 978-0439-96512-5

ISBN 0-439-96513-6
ISBN 978-0439-96513-2

ISBN 0-439-96514-4
ISBN 978-0439-96514-9

ISBN 0-439-965152
ISBN 978-0439-96515-6

ISBN 0-439-965160
ISBN 978-0439-96516-3

ISBN 0-439-965179
ISBN 978-0439-96517-0

ISBN 0-439-965187
ISBN 978-0439-96518-7